INVASION OF THE RUBBERNECKS

INVASION OF THE RUBBERNECKS

Spinechilling Times in Soho

by
Mark Jones

CENTURY
LONDON   SYDNEY   AUCKLAND   JOHANNESBURG

Published in Great Britain in 1990 by Century
An imprint of Random Century Ltd
20 Vauxhall Bridge Road, London SW1V 2SA

Century Hutchinson Australia (Pty) Ltd
20 Alfred Street, Milsons Point, Sydney, NSW 2061, Australia

Century Hutchinson New Zealand Ltd
PO Box 40-086, 32-34 View Road, Glenfield, Auckland 10, New Zealand

Century Hutchinson South Africa (Pty) Ltd
PO Box 337, Bergvlei 2012, South Africa

Set in Linotronic Garamond No. 3

Printed and bound in Great Britain by Mackays of Chatham, Kent

British Library Cataloguing in Publication data
Jones, Mark
    Invasion of the rubbernecks : spinechilling times in Soho.
    1. London. Westminster (London Borough). Soho – Visitors' guides
    I. Title   914.2132

ISBN 0-7126-3457-6

PREFACE

The world is competitive and tonight I am a competition winner. The prize for being a young journalist on the make is to be a specially invited guest at a celebrity party. The losers in the dark business suits will spend the evening draughtily in Covent Garden or impatiently waiting for a table in Soho while I have champagne urged upon me when my glass is still three-quarters full and dine splendidly off prunes filled with cream cheese and roulades of salmon mousse and brown bread. I will taste titbits of gossip with the titbits of food and there will be titbitty conversations with the famous and notorious, and tomorrow the columns I write for will be gorged with delicious morsels.

I walk through the lobby of the hotel. You don't quite get the red carpet treatment here, but you do get the red and turquoise swirly carpet treatment, which will have to do.

1

By the ballroom entrance I am accosted by a woman in black whose short, white hair makes her look like Annie Lennox seeing a ghost.

"Over here," she says with a come hither look. I go thither.

Close up, her smile has about as much come-hitherness as an air hostess's; in fact, an air hostess would be shocked by its obvious insincerity. She produces a list.

"Welcome to the launch. If you'd just put your name there."

I write my name, rank and newspaper while absorbing the names of guests accosted before me. A waste of time, really, as anyone famous will have gone through with a nod and an admiring gasp.

She peers at my name, her head tilted on one side, her face close to mine; so I wiggle my eyebrows at her.

"An alias. Just let Mick and Jerry know I'm here and tell the Princess I'll see her afterwards."

"Ha, ha," she says.

The familiar sound of liggers getting into their stride wafts up from the ballroom.

"It sounds lively," I say.

"It is," she assures me, bored.

"Who's here?"

"Everyone."

"Ah, Everyone. How nice for them."

As I turn towards the kerfuffle, the accosting girl suddenly presents her neck to me, craning within inches of my mouth, her shoulder brushing the buttons of my jacket. I step back, surprised, wondering if this is a sacrificial, erotic gesture of atonement for her indifference to my wiggling and smooth conversation. But she is peering around the corner of the corridor.

Then she steps back. There is a half-excited, half-terrified look on her face. The efficient, hard-mouthed stewardess of five minutes ago has vacated the body in the short black skirt, leaving it to a knickers-wetting teenybopper. Obviously, there is a star on the way.

Sure enough, Bill Wyman rounds the final bend surrounded by a small band of courtiers. There is no sign of his wife; it is probably too late for her to be up.

The paparazzi, who have been sitting around the lobby with their customary air of sneering boredom, spring to their feet with as much athleticism as lenses, bulbs, heavy leather jackets, beer guts and gold jewellery will allow. Bill walks past, a slight, young figure with his jeans and trainers: the face is that of a middle-aged businessman. He smiles stoically at the photographers and the accosting girl, who looks as if she cannot decide whether to scream or curtsey.

Bill's smile evaporates when one of the paps comes over and puts a leather-jacketed arm around his shoulders. This offends the courtiers, who regard Bill's shoulder as sacred ground. The pap is Nick the Greek, the only man I know whose face can simultaneously be covered in designer stubble *and* aftershave. Nick is not the hard-bitten, seen-it-all type. Nick is an enthusiast, an optimist who believes that the stars are as eager to see him as he is to earn £200 by snapping them.

"Hiya, Bill! Saw you at the weekend down at Cliveden, but didn't get the chance to say hello. Nice one. Good do. How you doing? How's Mandy?"

"Ah," says Bill.

They wander downstairs, Nick chatting earnestly, while Bill seems to prefer the company of the wall.

I compose myself to follow them down to the snake pit.
Give me a whip, a hat, a distressed leather jacket and a sound-
track by John Williams and I could be Indiana Jones about to
confront an evil, man-eating cult.

*

Before me, some three hundred people are writhing together.
There is a gap of only a few inches between individual writh-
ers, allowing little room for the waitresses to squeeze between
them and even less for the pecks and embraces the guests keep
giving each other. It is like the rush-hour tube without the
newspapers and with a lot more Chanel Number 5.

Much of the writhing stems from the upper halves of the
guests. Wherever you look, heads turn, necks stretch, noses
point and chins tilt. As Wyman moves through the crowd,
heads follow him like a Mexican Wave.

I am supposed to know dozens of people here. As it turns
out, I know no one; that is, I recognise everyone and know no
one. Glum-faced journalists are butting into the private conversations of Marie Helvin, Viscount Weymouth, Auberon
Waugh and other top-of-division-two celebs. I do not behave
in this tiresome manner. Out of shyness, not delicacy. I'll
have to make something up for the morning edition.

I sidle, nibble, sip and glance for 20 minutes or more, feeling superior and isolated by turns. Sometimes I hate these
parties; sometimes I wish I were at Tutton's with the young
men and women in the dark, pleated suits or in some foul
Northern pub getting ratted like the other good blokes.

Then a figure in a bright green suit detaches itself from the
writhing and attaches itself to me.

"Mark! A thousand greetings from the land of the lost souls!"

This is Tristram. Trist is not one of your modern public relations men, all Positioning, Strategic thinking and Thomas Pink shirts. He is an old-fashioned, utterly trashy publicist: a manipulator, a stunt-puller, a sycophant, a sneak, an untrustworthy fellow and, it goes without saying, a consummate charmer. He smiles a sickly smile, revealing a combination of gold and bad teeth.

I give him the standard greeting used by journalists to PR men.

"Hello, you oily rat. Kiss my arse and order a bottle of Krug and make it snappy."

"Right you are, Oh Worshipful Gutter Hack." He runs a tongue around lips that stand out unnaturally red against his pale complexion. As he speaks, he transfers his gaze from left to right, peers around me and above me to catch the new arrivals.

"Who's here?"

"No one really," he says. But his pop eyes pick out someone in the writhing mass.

"There's Angie. Got to lig. Keep rubbernecking, darling."

Tristram flashes a quick smile, then looks at me with a strange intentness, as if wondering why I am here. As he goes, he raises his arm above the heads of the guests and makes his fingers into a snake's head. The fingers hang in the air twisting, darting, peering, circling. Then the snake is sucked gently back into the pit.

CHAPTER ONE

One of the games I play is to put my 17-year-old self in my shoes and see how he reacts to his surroundings.

The shoes in question are a pair of black Bass Weejun loafers and the first reaction of the 17-year-old self, beginning his scrutiny at the most southerly point, is to wonder why he is wearing a pair of bonehead slip-ons as if he's going to some Northern Soul joint. Where, he wants to know, are the old Dunlop pumps or the motorbike boots; and why are there not several inches of frayed denim encroaching on the toes of the said slip-ons? Above all, why is he wearing a suit? I tell him with humorous dignity that the suit is by Jasper Conran, but he is not impressed.

My 17-year-old self and me catch a glimpse of ourselves in the window of a guitar shop on the Charing Cross Road. To use one of his preferred phrases, he freaks out. Having stoutly fought off teachers, parents and split ends for several years, he is naturally anxious to know why a good ten inches have been lopped off his hair – presumably with the consent of the contemporary incumbent of his body. I try to explain that if you have long hair in 1988, at least, long hair uninhibited by hairdressers, dreadlocks or gel, you risk being mistaken for a lecturer in computer science. Again, he is not impressed. There is something in his manner which implies that I have copped out. It is never any use arguing with someone who thinks you've copped out, so we walk along in silence for a time.

The 17-year-old me knows that he is in London and this too surprises and saddens him. London is a place he abhors. To him, it is a place of loud, quick, unfriendly voices; cramped, uncomfortable places; mile after mile of identical tall buildings. He despises the anonymity of London; anonymity is what he fears. As a 17-year-old genius who will one day change the face of British rock music, and perhaps British poetry and cinema acting into the bargain, he cannot risk anonymity at this vulnerable stage in his career. So far, he has limited himself to major appearances with a Woolworth's acoustic guitar in front of the bedroom mirror.

The area of London we are walking through is one of the few he recognises: Soho.

My home is two miles to the north and my office is wherever I am covering or filing a story, but Soho is where enquiries should be addressed at most hours of the day or night.

Seventeen-year-old me still looks grumpy, so I continue. Mine is not the Soho of the Old Bohemian Farts, the Characters who meet in rat-arsed conspiracy in the Coach and Horses or The Colony Rooms, men whose faces speak not so much of the low life they have led as the years of telling the tales of their low life to impressionable features editors. And mine is not the Soho of the OBF's heirs, the young men whose own reputations as Characters are founded on the shabbiness of their tweed jackets, the vitriolic tone of their occasional articles in *The Spectator* or *The Daily Telegraph* and the brilliant novels they are alleged to be writing.

The 17-year-old self has switched off and is probably going over guitar solos in his head. But I am feeling too lyrical to stop now.

My Soho is the kingdom of black leather chairs and white tiled floors; of expensive restaurants staffed by drama students; of bars with more pot plants than bottles; of film companies, design consultancies, advertising agencies, PR outfits, fashion houses; of double-breasted suits, loud Christopher New ties, Chanel-style short-skirted suits. It is the Soho of contacts, deals and strategies. And it is the Soho of sex. Not dingy, furtive sex in dank bedrooms or blue-lit bars, but sex hinted at and understood in the midst of the deals and stratagems, sex to be contracted at leisure in clean, planned and designed rooms after taxi rides back to Fulham or Islington.

But the 17-year-old me saw another Soho and saw it through different eyes on a Saturday afternoon in 1976. He stepped off the train at Euston with seven other teenagers: five boys with bum fluff indifferently covering spotty chins and two girls with long, centre-parted hair and flowers embroidered on their jeans. They were on the way to a rock concert.

The boys were prone to manic fits of laughter and mimed guitar solos, shaking back their hair and pulling their faces into anguished expressions of heavy metal ecstasy. The girls stuck close together, whispering, sometimes laughing, but mostly with expressions quiet to the point of gravity.

This was a provincial, patriarchal society and we behaved according to the instincts bred into us for generations: so as soon as we set foot in London, we headed straight for Soho to see a dirty film.

The girls weren't very keen. Lorraine was the prettier and more solemn of the two. She had a smooth, white, not-fully formed face, what could be seen of it through the dark tangled curls, some of them dyed a russet colour, of her long hair. She had a tight, rather spiteful mouth and a haughty tendency to tilt her chin when speaking. She was tall, with a graceful neck. She was also my girlfriend.

"Let's not," she said to me as we crossed Leicester Square.

"Why not? Come on Lorraine, it'll be a laugh."

She put her hand through my arm and we must have looked odd in this middle-aged attitude in denim jackets and jeans plagued with badges and the names of groups copied from LP covers with a felt tip pen.

"Why don't just you and me have a wander. We'll meet the others after. We can see something of London. I want to go to Chelsea."

I, like Elvis Costello a couple of years later, didn't want to go to Chelsea, and I suddenly hated Lorraine for wanting something different to me. We had only been going out for two weeks.

One of the lads leant on our shoulders and inserted a hairy face between ours.

"None of this, ducks. You can get randy after the film, not before."

"Piss off, Dil," said Lorraine. "Well?" she said to me, no longer ingratiating.

"I think we should see the film," I said.

As I said, this was a primitive patriarchal society. I got my way.

*

As a concession, we agreed to see a film which, by virtue of soft focus camera shots and some even softer philosophising, was purporting to be an important statement in cinematic craft: the French film *Emmannuelle*.

This was a pivotal point in my education: the first time I saw pubic hair on a cinema screen.

The boys loudly applauded Sylvie Kristel's Path to Enlightenment through experiments with different combinations of male and female bodies. As film criticism, their observations were direct but to the point: "Gerremoff!" said someone superfluously at one point, adding "worrrrrr!" as the scene reached its inevitable conclusion. "Dive, baby, dive," said a would-be Barry Norman next to me.

Lorraine said she had, if I remember rightly, "bad vibes" about the cinema and the grey, litter-strewn street in which it stood. Throughout the film she sat sulking underneath her thick make-up, angrily shrugging away when I tried to put my arm around her shoulders.

"This is so boring," she finally said, as a long Lesbian scene with mawkish music and silly French whimpers got under way. "Does this really turn you boys on?"

Lorraine cast a dampener on our nervous high spirits. Sylvie and her friend were allowed to play out the scene uninterrupted. Half-way through, Lorraine got up with a heavy sigh, brushing off the hand I placed protectively on her arm.

She didn't come back. After 15 minutes, Karen, the other

girl, went to look for her. She also failed to make a re-appearance.

We left the cinema feeling thoroughly miserable. The manager told us we were a bunch of little gits, and we accepted the rebuke in silence.

Lorraine and Karen were not outside.

"They must have been really offended," said one of the bum fluffs.

"Karen was all right," said another, with a challenging look in my direction.

"Can't you control your woman proper?" said someone else to me.

"She said she wanted to go to Chelsea," I said weakly.

"Maybe that's what she did."

*

Lorraine and Karen were waiting for us at the concert. Lorraine wouldn't speak to anyone, least of all me. I tried again and again, apologising, entreating, joking: but she just looked ahead with fierce eyes and a hard look I had never seen before.

There was something sneering in that look, something contemptuous of the group of boys and of me in particular. I always remember that look and it is sometimes with me when I wander around Soho: the look in Lorraine's eyes after she was sexually assaulted in the toilets of a cinema off Leicester Square.

CHAPTER TWO

"Y ou wouldn't believe, watching that film, that Daniel Day-Lewis *hates* sex, would you?"

"I wouldn't believe it if you told me."

"You're so *sceptical* all the time, chicken. It isn't a very nice trait in such a young person."

We have just been to see *The Unbearable Lightness of Being*, one of those unlikely art house movies that become hits from time to time, pushed along in this instance by the generous helpings of explicit sex which the director offers along with the middle-European angst. Daniel Day-Lewis, playing a randy Czech doctor, gets more than a side order.

"When I were a lass, we didn't think much of lads as that took us to dirty films on t'first date," says Sally in a lamentable Yorkshire accent.

"This is not a dirty movie. This is *art*, damn it!"

Sally's voice becomes that of a literary critic on Radio Three.

"One sees the essential unity of the all-pervasive symbol of the doctor's hand going up the nurse's skirt, its psycho-cultural resonance with the political 'seduction' of late 1960s Czechoslovakia . . ."

Sally is a journalist, although that is much too prosaic a term to describe a woman who could give lessons in mischief to Pandora.

She writes for a diary column where her natural wit and ex-uberance are cruelly inhibited by the watchful body of lawyers who dog her every step, scissors in hand. The bow-dlerising of her copy does not worry her unduly, as, to Sally, her vocation consists of scaring the famous and celebrated witless with innuendo and gossip. "Who needs to write any-thing down?" she often says. "It's enough that you *might*."

Facts become elusive, playful creatures when they arrive in Sally's area of influence. She reports the lurid, the scandalous, the disgusting and the outrageous with a solemn assurance which fools nobody and which nobody dares to challenge.

But underneath is Sally the moralist, Sally the highly edu-cated Home Counties girl who despises the adulterers, loathes the arrivistes and hates the poseurs. The adulterers, the arrivistes and the poseurs do not know this dark, ethical side, nor do the Conservative politicians and media celebri-ties who are her regular dinner dates. All adore her un-questioningly, even – some say particularly – when she savages them.

*

We cross Shaftesbury Avenue in search of something hot and *nouvelle* on an octagonal plate. We settle on the Braganza in Frith Street; nowhere is the *cuisine* so *nouvelle* and nowhere do the plates look so much like something designed by a geometry professor.

It isn't Sally's kind of place at all, which is why, as the most contrary person in London, she suggests going there.

"I expect we'll see some of your fashionable friends there," she says.

The Brag is one of those places that goes in for blinding white tiles and blinding white walls.

We are led upstairs, feeling our way along the wall and shielding our eyes against the glare. The maitre d' doesn't think we are being very funny so Sally, who starts when other people think it's time to stop, asks if there is a guide dog in the house. The maitre d' smiles a twisted smile. With his black polo neck he looks like a villain in the early James Bond movies.

Sally sits on the edge of her seat with the sparkling, expectant expression she always wears in places where there might be celebrities to tease. We order a bottle of champagne and the points of her severely cut, Louise Brooks-style bobbed hair scan the adjoining tables like radar antennae. BEEP, she picks up Koo Stark and an Unknown Male in one corner, BEEP BEEP, a TV presenter in another. Her rather long nose twitches. She prods me in the knee with her fork and nods quickly in the direction of David Puttnam.

Puttnam doesn't know it, but he has chosen an unlucky evening to have dinner with Charles Saatchi.

David is getting excited about something: the decline of the English hedgerow, perhaps, or the Hollywood star system. He punctuates a comment forcefully and loudly by knocking his plate off the table. There is that moment of stifled silence you always get in these situations as everyone suppresses the urge to let out a huge schoolboy cheer. The waiters buzz around gathering new potatoes and material for future anecdotes. *Film producer in posh meal bust-up*. Sally looks on with the contented air of a Circe admiring the unwary mortal she is going to turn into a pig in tomorrow's column inches. Poor Puttnam. Something happens to the ions in the atmosphere when Sally is present.

*

Over the steamed turbot, Sally lays into the champagne. She gets tipsy easily, a weakness that is mercilessly exploited by despicable people like myself who like to see what trouble she will cause in her souped-up state.

Unfortunately, I am her first target.

"I want to know all about this girl from the advertising agency. The one you're pursuing," she says, sucking the cream from her long fingernails, which have unaccountably got dipped in the sauce on her plate.

I say nothing and look stern.

"Come on, Mark. Don't be shy. I know all about it. Five foot two, eyes of blue and oh, what those big boobs can do. Especially to a randy little chap like you."

I still say nothing, hoping that Puttnam will spare me by upsetting his coffee as well.

"Her name is Doreen, or something ridiculous like that. Posh voice with a slight American accent," she continues. "Although my sources say she is not exactly a *première cru* in terms of breeding. Which surprises me, because I always thought you liked" (back to Yorkshire accent) "a bit o'class."

"What do you mean, pursuing?"

"Well, chasing, following with amorous intent, that kind of thing. Having quiet dinners at Ma Cuisine, late drinks at the Groucho, grinning a lot, touching knees, looking dreamy. That kind of thing. Pursuing."

Sally leans over the table, chin resting in hand after one or two misses. She gazes at me, her eyes watery with drink, but still sparkling. Playing for time, I order another bottle.

The trouble is that Sally's sources are broadly accurate. There is a girl in an advertising agency. Her name is Lori, not Doreen and she is a good deal taller than five foot two (but I am big enough to accept that that item of information was only put in for the sake of Sally's rhyme). In all other respects, she is right. It grieves me to think I've been spotted grinning a lot and looking dreamy.

Pursuing is a risky business. Your dignity is on the line. Friends should learn of your intentions on a strict need-to-know basis. On the other hand, you desperately want some-one to confide in: someone to find out how the Pursued is taking your advances; and to give you a full pathologist's re-port on the skeletons in their cupboard.

But there are better people than Sally in whom to confide. The entire population of central London, for a start.

"I don't think you should jump to conclusions," I say, lamely.

"Oh God, this is serious." Sally falls back in her seat and gives me a reproachful look.

"Um," I say, pouring more drink.

Sally rises unsteadily.

"Off for a pee-pee," she says, attempting to plant a slob-bery kiss on my cheek and almost blinding me. "Only teas-ing," she adds, tripping over a waiter. It occurs to me that I love her: it does sometimes.

*

We drink and chat and the warmth created by the alcohol grows at the same rate as the warmth I feel for Sally: quickly.

We refuse coffee and carry on with champagne and talk about journalists. But not, thankfully, the crap journalists usually talk about each other.

Our main subject is Glotter. Glotter is a reporter on industrial affairs on Sally's paper and is a founder member of the Dishonourable Society of Old Fleet Street Lags. The Society is made up of soaks who, in the great Fleet Street tradition, have lied, flattered and bullied their way into positions of power, positions where writing ability means nothing and a carbuncle tenacity is all that matters.

Glotter is well into his sixties, has papery skin, a pot-belly, bloodshot eyes and hair greased back with something that turns the white locks a dirty nicotine colour. He enjoys the company of young journalists.

Sally and me both served our apprenticeship under Glotter. In other words, we have been forced to sit for hours in pubs that smell of disinfectant listening to him ramble on about the good, rough old days on the good old local paper, about the time good old Jock, the news editor, made him rewrite a story twenty times in an evening or the occasion when good old Jake, the sports editor, sacked a junior reporter having first vomited over the man's desk. Then there were the stories about Beaverbrook who, despite ample illustrations of his fascism, insanity and boorishness, always turns out to be "The Beaver. A grand old man. The best. There'll never be another like him." We young university-educated journalists stared red-faced into our half pints.

"The thing about Glotter's mob," I say, "is that for all their machismo they are so childish and sentimental. They pretend there's all this Honour Among Thieves and that they're all such Lovable Rogues, and all the time they're sharpening the knives for the next back-stabbing binge. Honour among journalists disappeared on the night a reporter bribed one of Cleopatra's maids to sneak into the chamber before she put the asp down her bra —"

Sally butts in.

"So scooping the rival papyrus for the big *Topless Royal in Snake Death Pact* exclusive. You've told me that one before. But you probably haven't heard about the latest outbreak of the Glotter virus. You're looking at an infected woman. Glotter tagged on to us after we'd been to this book launch," she says. "Thanks to my criminal weakness, we all ended up back at my flat afterwards for a few drinks, the odd character assassination, the usual. Glotter being unbearable, five Beaver anecdotes et cetera et boring cetera.

Finally, I got rid of them at about three in the morning. Or so I thought. I was just collecting the clean nightie and face pack before going to bed when this *hideous* figure lurches out of the bedroom."

"That hideous figure can only be one hideous figure."

"Glotter. Naked. Not a stitch. It was *disgusting*. I shall never look at the male body in the same way again. I thought only women wobbled when they walked. There he was with his little willy wiggling with excitement under his pot belly. He tries to take me in his arms and says" (cue gruff Cockney accent) " 'Shall, duck, yer know oi've always loved yer. The time 'as come, baby. Come to me.' "

"You're making this up. This is the same Glotter who tried to get you sacked a couple of months ago."

"Shut up, I'm not making anything up. 'Come to me,' he says, wiggle, wiggle, and then makes another lunge."

"What did you do?"

"Screamed, of course. Loud. That didn't do any good so I told him if he laid his foul paws on me then *Private Eye* and anyone else who's interested could have the story, *complete* with a full description of his manly dimensions."

"And that worked."

"It made him think a bit."

"But he is married, isn't he?"

"Of course he's married. But men like Glotter only think of their wives when their bellies are empty and it happens to be one of those rare occasions when they've managed to drag their bloated bodies home because no one will put up with them at work."

"But you got rid of him in the end."

"Eventually, I just threw his clothes out of the window so he had to go wiggling out into the street after them."

We both laugh hysterically, to the annoyance of the manager who doesn't want to upset his famous guests. He's probably had a word with the restaurant's PR man and the press photographer should already be on his way to snap them as they leave.

But not before Sally has finished with them. Her methods for getting a story are admirably direct.

She wanders over towards the young TV presenter who is having dinner with the kind of not-entirely-natural blonde young TV presenters do have dinners with. She plants herself on his lap, puts her arms around his neck and puts her cheek affectionately next to his. She beckons me over to join her by waving a stockinged toe in the air. There is nothing to do but obey.

"Mark, this is Jason. Isn't he gorgeous?"

"Very gorgeous," I agree. Indeed, he is handsome in that uncomplicated way that TV presenters are handsome. And he gives me that pitying look that TV people give print journalists and I give him that look of professional disdain that print journalists give TV people. I introduce myself to the bimbo, who looks sulky.

Jason spots this and politely asks Sally to remove herself from his knee, "before the photographer you've no doubt briefed in advance sees us". Sally leans back, cupping his chin in her hands, and gazes at him as a mother might at her child prodigy.

"Jasey! Isn't he adorable?"

Jasey accepts the compliment equably. I am beginning to get irritated with this dressmaker's dummy of a journalist.

"Come on Sally. Don't be a teenybopper," I say, helping her down from her perch.

"Weeeee!" she says, sliding gracefully to the floor. Jason looks nervously around. The bimbo bites her lip.

I help Sally up and she leans on Jason's shoulder, regarding him speculatively.

"By the way," she says, "I heard such a funny thing about you yesterday. About a little film you made while you were at Oxford."

"A film?" he says with forced puzzlement.

"Yes, you remember. The one with the rude scenes in it. Don't you remember all the trouble you went to to find the right girl to play the rude scenes? I hear there was a veritable queue of nubile undergraduettes outside your door."

"What rubbish," he says in a tone which is as good as a confession to our trained ears.

"Yes, I'm sure, darling," says Sally, patting him inexpertly on the head and so ruining the laborious efforts of three ITV hairdressers. "I'll give you a ring tomorrow and you can tell me what rubbish it is. Lovely to meet you," she says offering her hand to the bimbo. The bimbo tries to think of something brilliant and catty to say, doesn't come within a hundred miles, and settles for a sarcastic smile instead. Jason follows Sally with eyes that are at once admiring and full of trepidation as she goes back to our table.

*

The Soho night is so clear and neon-lit that it is really not dark. The dark-suited boys and girls are competing for taxis, there is manic jazz coming from Ronnie Scott's and there are policemen on the street looking for drunk Northerners. The May night is so warm that we could go for a walk across country, collapse in a haystack and say lyrical things about the moon. But there are no fields or haystacks in Soho and the moon looks like a rogue full-stop from an ad in Piccadilly Circus.

I am tired and woozy, but I don't want the evening to end.

"Shall we go to a club?" I ask Sally.

"You mean one of those places where you have to listen to people with speech impediments talking over a lot of drums while men with earrings show off their bottoms?"

"That's it."

"I can't think of anything more loathsome. But you go, you fearless young trend setter."

"I don't know a club where you can dance to Mozart. Sorry."

"Well, there should be one. I like dancing to Mozart when I'm doing the ironing."

"What about the Filipino maid? I thought she did the ironing."

"She does, really. I was just making a pathetic attempt to

21

make you think that I'm a homely, down-to-earth girl at heart, not" (return to Yorkshire accent) "one of those Southern flibbertigibbets."

As we wander along Old Compton Street, an old man in a filthy raincoat holds out a dirty, calloused hand to us. His eyes are watery and pleading and he says something like "Worragorra10pfockworr?"

I give him a pound coin as Sally removes herself to the other side of the road. The beggar says something like "Worragorratafockgorra" and lurches off towards some dark-suited boys and girls.

Sally is staring into the window of a clothes shop as I cross to her.

"Anything up?" I say, brightly.

"Not really. Is your conscience feeling better now?"

"Oh yes. I feel a real Mother Theresa among journalists."

"After an £80 meal."

Sally goes over to negotiate with the driver who looks her up and down with a not-very-attractive smile as she crosses. I run over as she gets in.

"We appear to be parting on bad terms and I don't really know why," I say, holding the top of the door.

I pull my fingers away as she slams the door.

"Perhaps it's because I don't want to go to bed with you," she says.

CHAPTER THREE

Talks between Miss Sally Bretforton and Mr Mark J collapsed amid mutual recriminations and scenes of chaos last night.

Mr J was the first to comment on the abrupt breakdown.

"Things went really well at first," he said. "Substantial progress was made on a range of issues, including the morals of TV presenters and restaurant decor. However, Miss Bretforton suddenly decided to terminate the meeting at around 11.30 pm. I have no idea why."

Our political correspondent adds: Inside sources believe the sudden collapse of the meeting was precipitated by the issue of social policy, and in particular Mr J's liberal attitude towards the homeless and alcoholic. Miss Bretforton's strong line on these and similar issues is well known.

Another area of speculation is sex. Mr J's alleged involvement with an unknown person described by Miss Bretforton as "a floozy from an advertising agency" could well be behind last night's extraordinary events, although further details are as yet unavailable.

Mr J says that he is anxious to arrange another meeting in the near future. However, experts who have studied Miss Bretforton's behaviour in the past think he will in all likelihood have to sweat it out for longer than he thinks.

CHAPTER FOUR

The man in the bright checked jacket carefully puts down his glass. He takes off the jacket, folds it across his arm and turns square on to me.

"Come on then. Justify what you do. Justify it. You can't. You know why? Because you're a sneak. The worst kind of sneak, running back with miserable little tales to your editor, hoping he'll give you a gold star for being a good little boy. Worried that he might take your pants down and give you a spank if it isn't squalid enough. Come on. Justify yourself."

"Do we know each other?"

He shifts the jacket to the other arm and lets out an angry sigh. His fists are clenched white.

"I don't want to hear you, because I know what you're going to say. You're going to get pompous and start going on about professional integrity and the public's right to know, all that crap. The right to peddle crap. The right to pry and

25

sneak. And bribe. It's not so much my right to privacy. It's your right to *be* that bothers me."

"I have never dropped anyone in it or extracted information from someone who doesn't want to give it."

"Crap. Bloody crap. You're probably doing it now."

The man has been speaking loudly already; now he gets louder as he spots Ursula.

"Hey, Ursula, I hope you haven't got anyone here with a nervous disposition because we've got a fucking reptile here tonight."

"I know. Be kind to Graham, Mark. He's got a thing about journalists."

"Oh, Mark's being very nice. Listening politely, all smiles, very gentlemanly. But you wait till the paper appears tomorrow."

*

A Friday night party for television and advertising people who have made more money than is good for them. This is Fulham, in one of those backstreets which in Manchester would make a good substitute for the *Coronation Street* set but where Londoners are more used to the living standards of *Dallas*.

The living room has the impersonality of an art gallery and as many pictures; the sterilised air of a recording studio with as much sound equipment; the uncomfortable air of a design consultancy and it is just as over-designed.

*

"I have this friend, all right. You know what the bastard

photographers did? They pulled him off his bloody motor-bike. To get a picture . . . right, to get a picture. I suppose *that's* the freedom of the press."

"Graham, leave Mark alone and let him enjoy the party."

"Why? His friends wouldn't let my friend alone."

"They weren't your friends, were they, Mark?"

"I'll tell you what else they did. There was this kid, about ten or eleven. Really early on Saturday morning, he rings the bell. Paul goes down in his dressing gown. The kid asks Paul if he can clean his car. Paul says no, thanks, pat on the head all the same. And just as he's about to close the door the kid jumps aside and the photographers start clicking. All because he didn't want his picture taken for some bunch of lies they were writing about him. How are your professional ethics, matey? Ever bribe any ten year olds?"

I get away from the loud jacket and find a peaceful grove next to the olives and crisps.

*

"I know. Brilliant just isn't the word for Spielberg. I mean, he's gone way beyond. No one, but no one says so much in a single frame. You know, if I had one of those time capsules, I'd put in a Spielberg movie and leave it at that. I mean, that's all anyone in the future will want to know about us. It's all there."

"What about Bergman or Fellini?"

"Oh, they're marvellous, of course, but so *slow*. Have you ever sat through a Bergman? Christ. And, I don't know, they don't have the *depth* of Stephen's work."

Oh dear, she has used the Christian name and someone has fallen for it.

"Reeney, didn't you meet Spielberg once?"

"Oh, I haven't seen Stephen in ages. I keep meaning to keep in touch. Yes. I met him at a party in LA. I know it's a cliché and everything, but he is a *really nice man*. Not at all affected, even though he's so rich. I mean, you wouldn't believe it."

"Quiet?"

"Sure. Kind of intense. But really nice."

"What did you talk about?"

"This and that. The movies. Just a nice quiet chat. Really charming."

"I'm sorry to speak this way about a close friend of yours, but I'm not sure about your time capsule idea. I don't know if I'd like my period in history to be summed up by a few children's films."

Spielberg's friend looks at me venomously.

"Bravo, Mark. It's a good job they don't let you near the film pages, isn't it? Just pray that you can achieve a millionth of what that man's done."

*

"You're a Sagittarius, right? It positively seeps from you. I feel very close to Sagittarians. I empathise with them so well. You are one, aren't you?"

"Not exactly. But I thought you said you were close to trees."

"I am close to trees. Trees and Sagittarians."

I look into the girl's stoned eyes and suddenly feel like slapping her. I say:

"Listen, let's stop. I don't know who's taking the piss any longer."

"Why are journalists always so cynical?"

"I don't think I'm cynical. Not cynical at all. Do you know what the word means?"

"Sure. Don't patronise. You're so negative."

"Well, if I've damaged your vibes, then sorry. I'm going for a pee."

*

"I bet if you made a list of all the people who'd been hounded to death by journalists, there'd be more than the poor buggers who died in Auschwitz."

"That's sick and silly, Graham."

"And I'm Jewish and I can do without comments like that."

"I'm a journalist and I can do without them too."

Graham takes a deep drag from his cigarette, breathes deep and exhales a gust of words.

"Oh, you're back, are you, Mr Honourable Investigative journalist? Well, I'm not joking and this is for your benefit. Look at the news recently. There was that priest in Oxford who killed himself. He was blackmailed by newspapers, right, because they knew he'd written some controversial document or other."

"The Preface to *Crockfords*. Blackmail is a bit strong."

"A bit strong for him, too. He topped himself. Last week, I heard about this teenage boy who had hair all over his body. Your mates thought that was a good story too. *We Track Down Teenage Werewolf*. That's right, they did track him down. They hunted him into a corner and he hanged himself."

The people around are talking together in low voices.

There is spittle on Graham's beard. Ursula tries to calm him down, but he talks loudly and angrily over her quiet pleas.

"And Russell Harty. Everyone knows it was sodding journos who killed him. Fucking journos creeping around his bed at the end. Let him die in peace? Would they fuck. Too much of a *fucking good story*, matey, wasn't it?" He punctuates the words on my chest with his forefinger. People around are looking frightened. I am frightened.

"Listen, cool it. People have been saying these things for ages, ever since Shelley claimed it was reviewers who drove Keats to his grave." Graham throws down his cigarette impatiently. I try to speak in a measured voice.

"I agree, some journalists go too far, and I won't even claim that it's because their readers want them to go too far and buy more copies when they do. But listen, the kind of reporters you're talking about really are a minority. I know that makes them sound like football supporters . . ."

It sounds lame. I sense people's critical eyes on me and I blush.

"Listen to me, matey. Watch my lips," he says in a soft voice. "There are lots of different kinds of snake, but they all bite."

"Come for a bite to eat, Mark," says Ursuala, missing the pun and hustling me away.

*

We pass the open door. A young man with disordered curly hair and a thin, miserable face is sitting on the stairs.

"Who is that poser?"

"That's Angel. He isn't posing. He's sitting outside

because he says he gets very bored by media people and thinks he might say something rude if he comes in."

"He can't get much ruder than that Graham bloke."

"I know, Mark, I'm sorry, but you must admit that some journalists *are* naughty."

"Naughty, but not murderous."

"Yes, well. Oh, I think Angel wants me to go and speak to him."

I look at Angel with a violent loathing.

"Why don't you just let him wallow in his adolescence? It's the worst behaviour I've ever seen. If he hates everyone here, why doesn't he just fuck off?"

To my amazement, Ursula puts her bony hands on my lapels and pushes me roughly against the wall.

"I'll tell you why, Mark." Her face is close to mine and her teeth are bared. "Because Angel has come to see *me*, unlike everyone else in that damn room, including you. Go and get yourself a drink, if you like."

*

"Cannes? Boring. No one there. Weather gloomy. The French were as rude as ever."

"Any scandal, Sophie? You usually know."

"I saw Don manhandling Ursula, but there's nothing new in that. There was this appalling girl from WWT who flaunted herself at the Martinez every night."

"There's always one, at least one. Who was she?"

"Lori something. Tall, dyed hair, quite nice-looking in a tarty sort of way. I mean, it's hard to dress outrageously in Cannes, but she seemed to manage."

"I don't think I know her."

"Here's someone who does. Mark, you know that Lori girl, don't you?"

"Does she work for an advertising agency?"

"Yes, that's her. I was just telling Barry how she flaunted everything she had at Cannes last week."

"Really? I suppose she can be a bit of a flaunter, what I know of her."

"*A bit*. Come on, Mark, you're no fun. You're supposed to exaggerate things, not the other way round."

"I've never seen her go beyond the flaunting stage."

"No, Mark, I'm *sure* she's not that kind of girl."

Sophie grips her friend's arm and laughs unpleasantly.

"Stop tittering, Sophie," says a girl I don't recognise. "She's obviously his kind of girl."

"Come off it, darling. She's not nearly classy enough for Mark, is she darling?"

*

"Adrian would love to do another *Fatal Attraction*, but you don't get scripts like that a dime to the dozen. And you don't get Douglas and Darryl every day of the week."

"I heard he was going to do a comedy."

"Adrian? Don't make me laugh. I've known him for years and I've never seen him smile."

"Maybe you're right. He looked very long-faced when you went up to his table at the Caprice the other night."

*

"And the Duchess of Windsor. You know, they used to climb over the wall of her château in Paris. They used to try to get photographs of her undressing. I mean, how low can you get? I read somewhere that it made her so depressed she killed herself." Graham spots me trying to escape. "Listen, stop running away, smoothie. I'm talking to you."

I have had enough.

"No, let's get this right. You're the one who's keen on accuracy. You're not talking to me, you're shouting at me and you're being a fucking bore."

Graham grins and lays down his jacket. I cannot stop myself from fighting my losing battle.

"You've been a complete prat tonight. You think you're the great amateur moralist. Just because one of your friends may have been doorstepped once you make anyone who's ever written for any newspaper sound like a child molester. What do you want – a Police State? You don't want anyone to ask any awkward questions? You want nice little puffy stories for your friends, or what? What do you want?"

Graham is still smiling.

"Go on, throw another wobbly if you want. You've ruined the fucking party anyway."

"Cool it, Graham. Shut up, Mark."

"You make ads, don't you, Graham? Of course, that is a hundred times more ethical than what I do. I mean, you're only telling people what they want to hear, aren't you? Calmly presented, balanced information that makes us all better people, right, Graham?"

Graham has been perched on a table watching me with that shark grin. Now he takes a step towards me and puts an arm around my shoulders. His hot, bearded face is close to mine and he smells of sweat.

"Just come over here with me for a second. Come on, mate, I won't bite."

His arm still around me, we walk to the table. As we reach it, he suddenly grasps my hand and forces it to the table. Before I can react, he picks up a fork and jabs it hard into my forearm, twists it, takes it out and licks it clean. He smiles at me.

CHAPTER FIVE

I wonder if an injection of liver pâté or whatever glutinous substance was on the fork can give you blood poisoning. I wonder if the rip in the arm of my jacket can be stitched up. I wonder if anyone else has ever been stabbed in the underside of the arm with a white-handled David Mellor fork.

I am outside in the cold night now, thank God. It wasn't easy to escape the ogling curiosity of the helpers and the silence of the uninvolved, watching, not missing anything, drawing their conclusions.

Graham was taken upstairs to be calmed down, although he seemed perfectly calm to me. Psychopathic, but calm. Someone suggested calling the police, which made poor Ursula panic; the police might damage her party propaganda machine. Nothing offends the ambitious hostess so much as a few rozzers on the premises. Her relief when I told her I wasn't going to press charges was sickening to witness. This affected me strangely. For the first time since that weird, fixed moment when I stood next to Graham, watching him as he pressed the fork into my flesh I had to half-close my eyes to keep back the welling tears.

I had said I wanted to go. We had embraced clumsily. We both said sorry simultaneously, then there was another collision of words as Ursula said "Sure you'll be all right?" and I said "Don't worry, I'll be all right." She patted me awkwardly on the shoulder and out I went. Angel was still sitting on the stairs by the front door. He turned his stupid head towards me, elbows on knees, fingers resting in the thick, artistically cut hair. He gave me a feeble smile as I opened the door. If there had been a white-handled fork nearby I should have stabbed him.

Violent night, violent night.

*

I am walking along the Embankment. I will walk back to Islington and think. The pain in my arm, stabbing now I am outside, alone, will help me to concentrate.

I walk with only the incessant traffic for company. Past the gaudy lights on Albert Bridge, turned into pastels by the slow Thames, a designer river if ever there was one. Behind, Battersea is dark and secret. There is even a star or two, dim through the orange air of a London night.

In the country, the stars are cold and clear and you walk along dark lanes to the pub with cold and clear air inside you. In London, you let this orange, close air inside reluctantly and you wonder about wearing a mask to ease the traffic congestion in your lungs. In the country, you can hear your own footsteps. In the country, sounds are sharp on the night air, not crowded out by the monotonous woosh made by the 531,000 cars that pass daily through central London.

London is no good. You get tired of London and if that means you're tired of life then you have to find life elsewhere. You can't go on living in a place where people attack you with cutlery because they object to the job you do. You can't go to parties and ask the hostess to lock up anything sharper than a pepper mill beforehand and demand that the guest list be vetted for potential psychopaths.

And I can't go to places where I might meet anyone who witnessed my humiliation tonight. Anyone who heard me say no, it's all right, he's just upset, I don't mind, it doesn't matter. I'll walk home, honestly, it's only seven or eight miles. And I can't get over the feeling that I should have laid the bastard out.

London is no good. I will go and live in the country.

*

The City. There are just a few cars and buses around and the tall grey buildings block out the full moon. London hems you in. Beyond this gatehouse cluster of monoliths there ought to be open country and stars. Instead, there is another 15 or 20 miles of houses and roads and traffic lights and shops.

I am taking the long way round, but anything is better than going through Soho. It is 11.30: Soho will be at its most jostling and people will be hunting in packs for taxis. In Shaftesbury Avenue it will be like Saturday afternoon in any respectable country town.

Soho also makes me think of dangerous people, borderline cases who carry lethal pieces of Sheffield steel in the pockets of their leather jackets. And Soho is full of restaurants which, as everyone knows, are positive armouries for the upwardly mobile maniac. And in Soho there are girls causing mischief and accusing you of wanting to sleep with them even though not a word of seduction passes your lips. It is a place of temptation for wholesome girls who work in advertising agencies. Much better to take a girl from an advertising agency, settle in Wiltshire, make butter and keep a goat.

The tall, dignified quiet of the City is broken only by the homely sound of retching and cheering as a Hooray broker is sick on the steps of the Bank of England, encouraged noisily by his two mates. Good on you, lads. Nothing beats a spot of healthy male bonding. Beats sex any day. There ought to be posters warning against women, with little arrows pointing out that they cause hair loss, alcoholism, constipation and bouts of insanity. Women screw you up.

And tomorrow the Hooray brokers will go to their parents' houses in Wiltshire and Gloucestershire, wear their Barbours and take their dogs and hangovers for a walk. And in the evening they will sit down to dinner and use forks for putting food in their mouths.

I take off my jacket and roll up my shirt sleeve. The blood has run down my arm and congealed in four, just distinct rivulets.

*

Up the New North Road and I am knackered. Still there is the incessant woosh as some of the 531,000 cars go back to the suburbs or, lucky people, get out of town altogether. You don't get knackered in the country. You go for long walks and come back refreshed, that sort of thing.

And maybe he is right. Perhaps we are a gang of print assassins. Perhaps we are lechers and voyeurs.

*

Home. I will get up at 6 am and head for Wiltshire. I will make an offer on a cottage by the end of the week. I will worry about how I am going to earn enough money to live another time. The thing is to get out.

As a further act of defiance against London and all its works, I will not even play my Ansaphone messages. And I will not wash the wound in my arm, which will stay there as a reminder of an honourable battle, bravely fought and of a defeat accepted with humility and dignity.

*

6 am. 7.30. 9.15. 10. 10.30. 11.10. With a mighty bound, I free myself from bed. The blood on my arm has dried in picturesque fashion, but it doesn't look dangerous so I wash it off. The Ansaphone light is flashing.

"Mark, this is Ursula. Someone should explain about last night, but please, please, don't put this in your column. Graham is gay. He used to live with Paul Tomlinson, you know, the actor. I know him quite well myself – lovely man. Anyway, not so long ago, a couple of the papers got hold of this and hounded them half to death. Perhaps you remember the story: maybe some of your friends were involved. So Paul and Graham split up. Now Graham has heard that Paul is HIV positive.

"I don't know what else to say. I'm really sorry for what

39

happened, and Graham should never have done that. But you did goad him, you know. Hope you enjoyed the party. Bye."

CHAPTER SIX

am in the fast lane of the M4, going slowly. In front is
an Austin Allegro with a pipe in his mouth and an un-
flappable peace of mind which is apparent even from the
rear. Behind is a fuming BMW who, judging from his
driving, is about to explode in a cloud of steam.

The BMW and I jostle and swear for a few miles. Then I
turn off in the direction of my Dream Village. This is the village where I shall escape from London and mow lawns, join
the church choir and achieve a serenity experienced only by
Austin Allegro drivers.

But my mood is anything but serene as we trundle along
the Dream Lanes on the way to the Dream Village. My Golf
GTI also shows signs of irritability, despite the marvellous
views: views of the backs of tractors, the backs of sheep and
the backs of Austin Allegros. The sheep are particularly
defiant of the Highway Code with their habit of making

sharp right turns without indicating just as I am about to overtake.

By the time we pass the sign for Abbeybrooke, the Dream Village, it is 4 pm and we left London at 11.

But the sign is all we do pass. There is a long queue of other Dreamers waiting to drive into the village. We lurch along in first gear, with the Golf becoming thoroughly objectionable, for one whole side of a Grace Jones tape. Grace sings well about the stresses of living in New York, but it seems they are as nothing compared to the stresses of living in Abbeybrooke. New York, for example, does not have a traffic problem like this.

Grace is just clearing her throat for the start of side two when we reach the centre of the village. It is dominated by a circular, thatched medieval structure. Once, people bought and sold goats, turnips and holy relics here. Today, it is given over to the ancient Wiltshire craft of graffiti and some of the more prominent local artists are sitting on motorbikes next to their handiwork. I cannot hear them because of the noise made by the cars and motorbikes, but I imagine they are discussing the cost of spray paint and the size of their Arts Council grants.

My hotel is next door, but parking there is impossible without the aid of a giant can opener. Despite the best signwriting efforts of the hotel management, their car park is monopolised by clients of the establishment opposite. This is a thatched cottage with the Middle English name, Starz Video Bar.

Starz is doing a brisk trade. So is the enterprising villager who has established an improvised car park a quarter of a mile down the road on an area of grass usually reserved for the ducks who inhabit the neighbouring pond. The villager demands £2 an hour. I do not cough up graciously.

I lug my luggage up the hill back to the hotel. The graffiti artists break into laughter as I wait to cross the road outside Starz. One of them says something in a not very convincing accent that sounds like "okay, yah, great" as I jump between two cars. Then they all laugh again and one of them throws the butt end of a cigarette at my feet. I tuck my Liberty silk handkerchief out of sight in the pocket of my blazer and try to look hard and urban.

"Abbeybrooke Rotary Society Meets Here", says a sign on the hotel door. I utter a silent prayer: "Please, not tonight."

*

The hotel is built in a Cotswold stone darkened by the years or the constant stream of traffic. Inside, the reception area is done out in a thin white plaster embellished while wet by someone with an inventive mind and an old sponge. The pattern on the carpet is from an original design by Vesuvius. The mock beams shine with a fresh coat of matt black paint. Behind the smoked glass of the counter there is a computer, a screen, a printer, a photocopier and a fax machine.

I press the bell, which makes a noise like a police siren. After two or three minutes, it produces not the riot squad, but Mrs Youell, the manageress.

Mrs Youell is a small woman clad in what seems to be Wiltshire's entire crimplene production for the past year. Her hair is lacquered and bleached into a tinder-dry, petrified bun.

Her mouth cracks open in a thin smile, revealing dentures coated at the northern extremes with lipstick.

"Can I help you?" she says, adding, after a moment's hesitation, "sir?"

"The name is J. I've booked a room for the night."

"I know you have. And you're lucky to still have it."

"Am I?"

"Thought you was never coming. We're full tonight and I've had several enquiries about rooms. We expect guests to inform us if they're going to be late."

"I couldn't. I was in a traffic jam. Is it always like this?"

Mrs Youell looks out of the window and smacks her lips in ladylike disdain.

"Looks all right to me. It is Saturday afternoon, you know. And the village is a great attraction for Discerning Visitors. Park down by the pond, did you?"

"The ducks are probably letting down my tyres as we speak. Any chance of moving the car up here?"

"No."

"Ah. Why would that be?"

"We're very busy tonight. As I said, you're lucky to still have your room. There's an EastEnders evening in the bar and the Rotarians are meeting in the restaurant."

I sign the visitors' book with all the enthusiasm of King John endorsing the Magna Carta. Mrs Youell, eyebrows arched, regards the book critically.

"N1. We don't get many from round there, although one hears it's quite executive these days. My husband and I are from London originally. Holland Park West, Shepherd's Bush area."

"That's very executive. Why did you move down here?"

"Oh, we love it here. Wouldn't change it for the world. It's so peaceful and green."

I steal a quick glance through the frosted glass windows. If

Mrs Youell's idea of the verdant is anything like her notion of tranquillity, then the leaves should be painted a bright neon pink.

*

I go for a walk in the fields above the village, getting edited highlights of Wiltshire through the trees to the south as I go. A twinkling stream winds quietly through the valley. Beyond, the M4 winds rather less quietly towards Wales.

By Mrs Youell's standards, the stroll is very peaceful. That is, there is a four-piece family in matching red anoraks ahead; and in a procession coming towards me, a middle-aged couple in Barbours and walking boots; a teenage couple walking with difficulty because they have their arms entwined around one another; two men with a dog each; and one couple with one baby. Cans and crisp packets add a spot of colour to the scene. The graffiti artists, boldly venturing beyond the medieval market place, have sprayed endearments and profanities on the tree trunks. A fighter airplane screams above on its way to Salisbury Plain.

There is not much point in staying up here. Even the new wellies I bought especially for my new life have failed to acquire anything like an impressive coating of mud.

The teenagers who are trying to keep their balance while walking and slobbering over each other at the same time and one of the dog owners approach. Choosing my moment, I insert myself in the gap between dog and slobberers and make for the hotel. It is half past five and I am anxious to try Mrs Youell's home-made, genuine recipe for gin and tonic.

*

The bar of the hotel is not a place for migraine sufferers or anyone ideologically opposed to fruit machines. But the country theme has not been abandoned completely. Every available inch of white swirling wall is covered with a horse brass or a similar item of equestrian equipment, none of which has ever been within neighing distance of a horse. Somewhere in England there is a vast factory turning out these pieces of traditional junk exclusively for the pub market. No doubt its location is kept a close secret to deter arsonists from the paramilitary branch of the Campaign for Real Ale.

Dinner is Chicken Kiev in the basket. The basket is made out of plastic and the chicken doesn't look too promising either. I make an incision into the deep fried flesh and a stream of grey, garlic matter spurts on to my shirt.

My table is under siege from a riotous party of Rotarians. I am assailed by elbows, knees and shouted conversations within inches of my face as they try to weaken my resistance and force me to cede my territory. I determine to fight on.

Now the EastEnders party begins to arrive. Their main concession to cockney dress habits are trilbys and braces for the men and hats with plastic fruit on top for the women. If only they had employed me as their wardrobe consultant I could have put them right. The authentic look is lurex tracksuits or stone-washed denims. Dress codes have changed. To be accepted east of the City you need either the uniform of a New York breakdancing group or the £50 polo shirts popular among market makers and soccer hooligans.

A cheerful piano starts up. The EastEnders try to sing *On Mother Kelly's Doorstep*, but no one gets beyond the title. The pianist is persuaded to switch to a selection from *The Phantom of the Opera* and life becomes a dark and miserable thing.

The EastEnders have territorial ambitions of their own, but the Rotarians are determined not to relinquish an inch. I begin to feel like Poland, marooned between two formidable and aggressive powers. But unlike Poland, I decide to give up without a fight. I finish the chicken quickly; or, rather, I discard a half-eaten carcass with shreds of grey-brown meat clinging to it. Upstairs in my room is an improving book and a hip-flask of whisky, brought along to keep me going on the tough, eight-mile hike I intended to do this afternoon. I get up, and a Rotarian snatches the stool with the seat of my trousers still only a few inches clear.

But Abbeybrooke hasn't finished with me yet.

"Marcus!" A hand clasps me on the shoulder as I edge past the bar. With a heavy feeling, I turn around and see that the hand belongs to Soapy Cox, property consultant and one of Sally's legion of keen admirers. He is in the second division of those admirers, but pushing hard for promotion. "Well met, old son. What disgusting mission brings you down to these parts? Hang on, I'll get the drinks. Try the cider. Mrs Youell's home-grown."

Soapy is 6 ft 4, but has the pushiness of a much smaller man. In conversation, he has the disconcerting habit of bending his thin neck well inside the 20 inches exclusion zone and bestowing on you a sickly and attentive smile. He is tirelessly interested in everything you have been doing, exceptionally quick to laugh at your jokes and to sympathise with your problems.

He turns back from the bar and hands me a glass of liquid with the colour, opalescence and warmth of mature urine. He takes my elbow and guides me away from the front line where EastEnders and Rotarians are engaged in close hand-to-hand fighting for possession of the strategic ground in front of the bar.

"Of course I know why you're here, Marcus. How stupid. Sally-o said you were popping down to do some kind of article on the place. Didn't she mention that my folks had a place down here?"

"Funnily enough, she didn't. She must have forgotten."

"Gosh, that girl."

"I'm supposed to be down here for pleasure alone, but the message obviously didn't reach the chef."

"You should have come over to the ancestral home. Would have loved to see you." Soapy cranes his neck even closer and gives me a conspiratorial look. "But come on, Marcus, you're here on some kind of story, aren't you? I know you fellows. Never do anything for pleasure alone, not when there's money to be made. Look, the female brood are over in the corner. Come over and say hello."

Soapy leads me away from the pianist, who is trying to master the latest Kylie Minogue single. In the corner are two specimens of English upper-middle class womanhood. The one I don't recognise is quite pretty, or would be if it wasn't for her hair, clothes and smile, all three of which are silly and overdone. The hair is done in the bleached and dishevelled cavewoman-meets-Barbie-doll style; the pink jumpsuit glistens with sequins in unexpected places; and the smile is in the right place, but is fixed, toothy and too practised to inspire confidence. The specimen I do recognise is in tribal costume: striped shirt with collar up, pearls, pleated skirt, hair slide and badly applied make-up. This is Soapy's girlfriend, a thin-faced woman grown sour with years of having her delicate class sensibilities offended.

Least Pleasant and Most Perfunctory Exchange of Pleasantries Award

Gold medal: Julia "Smelly" Macdonald-Smith and Mark J, Abbeybrooke Arms, Wilts.

JULIA: Hello, Mark.
MARK: Hello, Julia.
SOAPY: Call her Smelly, Marcus.
JULIA: How's the journalism?
MARK: How's the polo equipment exporting business?
JULIA: Fine.

This exhausts the interest of Julia and myself in each other's recent history.

Meanwhile, the other specimen is waiting to be introduced. This is Caro, Soapy's sister. She shakes my hand vigorously and the encouraging smile intensifies, lowering my spirits still further. A horrible thought crosses my mind: that she is in public relations. She says brightly how she's always wanted to meet up, had heard loads about me and asks if I am still writing a column I gave up two years ago.

"Caro does the PR for that health club in Fulham you'll have heard about," says Soapy.

She doesn't hang around.

"That's right. *Mussels.* Mark, you *must* come down and see us. It's the first anyone has thought of combining a club and a restaurant – I mean a proper, cordon bleu restaurant – under one roof. It's a brilliant idea, they've had them in the States for years – I went to one owned by the parent company in LA last month, really advanced, *so* brilliant – and Carlos – he's the manager, he's really sweet and *incredibly* fit, God! What a hunk, isn't he Smelly? – anyway, he thought, why not do one here? I mean, it's just what the yuppy market's crying out for. Anyway, it's up and running – and the food – not just veggie stuff, all kinds of sumptuous things – is really good, it's all really nice . . ."

"I'm exhausted just hearing about it."

"No, but it's not really exhausting, not with the proper regime – and the instructors are *so* sweet, Mark – you just have to come down and see us. The chef is really, really brilliant, a real star. Come down for a work-out then lunch."

"It sounds like a recipe for indigestion."

"No, honestly, it's really refreshing and such a nice way to meet people – we've had Sam Fox and Anneka Rice and all sorts of people you'd like to meet there . . ."

Caro hypes on and on, suggesting that, whatever the tortures inflicted by her sweet instructors, nothing can be more punishing than an hour's PR work-out with her. So this is the Great Escape to the country: an evening spent hearing about some ghastly souped-up gym in Fulham.

We keep ordering more of Mrs Youell's samples of local pond life, apart from Caro who is keeping her mind clear so that she can talk crap. She sticks to mineral water.

Out of boredom, I begin to fancy her. Remove the layers of highly groomed PR executivism and you have something that is slim and quite palatable. I indicate the progress of my thinking by gazing at her with a touch of eyebrow-manoevring, while trying hard to make sure that the gaze denotes interest in Caro rather than her bloody health club. She carries on regardless. On reflection, the gaze is probably too glassy to denote very much, thanks to Mrs Youell's hell brew. I have to keep shaking my head to refocus the eyes and keep remembering to close my mouth when I'm listening to her.

Soapy and Smelly are standing at the bar, having tactfully left me to my interrogation. Soapy is earnestly stroking Smelly's buttocks through the pleated skirt and she looks very uncomfortable. Perhaps she envisages the day when she will be a permanent resident of Abbeybrooke and will have to come in to the pub and patronise everyone. This is so much more difficult to achieve if the rustic population has seen you standing at the bar having your bum rubbed on a Saturday night.

Soapy seems to notice something lascivious in my expression – which is more than Caro has done – and decides with brotherly zeal to interrupt.

"So Markey, tell us about this wonderful new bint you're seeing."

I turn my head lazily towards him. What a pain.

"Who?"

"That's what I'm asking."

I think for a moment.

"You must mean Sally."

Soapy's smile intensifies.

"Don't be silly, Marcus. I think you and I know that Sally has other fish to fry. What about this luscious advertising woman I've heard about?"

I look at him uncomprehendingly.

"No, there's no one I can think of. I'm sure you mean Sally."

Soapy's smile remains but there is hatred in his watchful eyes.

"I think that people would be very surprised if that was true, Marcus."

"Who's this Sally?" asks Caro, brightly.

CHAPTER SEVEN

Mr Mark J announced today that his plans to make a permanent home in the country have been indefinitely shelved. The news comes just two days after Mr J announced that he was quitting London for good after a violent incident at a party in the Fulham area.

In a brief statement issued from his position behind an Austin Allegro on the M4, Mr J said that "on mature reflection, I decided that my temperament could not withstand the intense pressures of country life. The situation will be reviewed at intervals, however."

Our J correspondent reports that the controversy surrounding his trip to the Wiltshire village of Abbeybrooke on Saturday is almost certainly behind today's shock announcement.

"The evening ended in some acrimony when J was accused of making a sexual advance at Miss Caroline Cox. The accusation was made by Miss Cox's brother, Mr Rupert Cox. Mr J violently disputed the charge and referred to Mr Cox in what eye and ear witnesses call 'right strong language, mate'. The dispute was settled by Mrs Norma Youell, landlady of the Abbeybrooke Arms, who threatened Mr J with ejection from the hotel premises if he didn't put a sock in it.

When asked for her reaction, Miss Cox said that your correspondent or any of his fellow reporters could take advantage of a free three-month trial membership of the Mussels Health and Gourmet Club in London SW6. Mr Cox was unavailable for comment."

CHAPTER EIGHT

My first move on returning to the capital is to request a meeting with Rodney. A formal application is made through the proper channels. The request is considered, granted and an appointment is made for the following Friday.

We convene in The Coach and Horses which is in Romilly Street, perhaps the most urinated-upon 50 yards in London.

The preliminary formalities are, as usual, lengthy. Rodney O'Connor is a thorough man and believes that such formalities must not be rushed. So we exchange notes on the quality of the beer, the situation in Iran, the biography of Bernard Shaw and the advisability of the barmaid's Mohican haircut. This last item provokes a lively debate but no firm conclusions. Finally, I feel able to raise the principal subject on the order sheet: my recent experiences in Fulham and Wiltshire.

Nothing beats feeling persecuted if you want to tell a good story. The tale of the several abuses I have suffered in the recent past comes rolling off the tongue and Rodney appears transfixed. At least, he appears as transfixed as a man can be who is absorbed in a pint of Ind Coope and a button that has worked loose from his tweed jacket.

I bring the narrative to an impressive close. Rodney takes a long draught of his pint, holds it up to the light and sighs.

"The man's a twat."

There is a pause while Rodney gazes quizzically across at the barmaid.

"Which man, Rodney?"

He looks at me with a pained expression.

"The man. Your fork man. The twat."

"And what about the property consultant?"

Rodney reflects for a moment.

"The man's a twat."

"They're both, then, twats?"

"Exactly. I don't want to malign the female anatomy. There are enough women doing that. Regretfully, no other word will do. Given the limited argot available to us, I've no choice or hesitation in describing the fork man and the other one as twats. Nothing else will do."

I listen to Rodney's speech respectfully. As a Ph.D and a lecturer at Birkbeck College, his views carry weight. If he calls someone a twat, he does not do so with the casual *élan* of a Smithfield porter or a Chelsea soccer fan.

Still, I feel my problem merits a more thorough answer.

"But you see why I got so depressed after the party?"

"Doing the work you do, I'm surprised that you're not in a state of continual depression. But the urge of the artistic soul to seek solitude and exile after an unpleasant incident is well known. Byron was doing the same when he ran off to Italy."

"So he was driven out by a psychopathic gay film maker as well?"

Rodney again subsides into silence. His are the most imposing silences in London. I feel that to break some of the deeper ones only something truly momentous will do, like a declaration of war or the announcement that the pub has run dry. At other times I just want to shake him furiously by the shoulders and scream "STOP PUTTING ON SUCH AN ACT, YOU ANTI-SOCIAL ACADEMIC GIT!!"

This isn't one of the worse ones. Rodney won't restart the conversation – God forfend – but a sly glance from time to time indicates that he's prepared to reopen the lines of communication.

"The thing is, Rodney, I really wanted to leave London, desperately. But after Abbeybrooke, I can't think of anything more hideous."

"You're not alone. Those of us who spend a sheltered life in the metropolis often find the demands of the country too much for them. Take this pub. An absolute model of the village inn. The clutch of weather-beaten regulars, the homely, rotting interior. Compare that with your Wiltshire hell-hole with its flashing machines, mock beams, business lunches, theme nights, party nights, God-knows-what-else-nights . . . it's hard to think of anything more stressful."

I know what he means. There is a soothing quality about the Coach after the hustle and bustle of Mrs Youell's empire. Tonight, as on most nights, there is the usual crew – the band of superannuated Soho ravers, all waiting to pounce on some innocent young journalist and bore him to death with tales of 1950s debauchery. These are the quaint, rustic souls who cross the boundaries of Soho into a neighbouring Parish on no more than three or four occasions a year, and beyond the boundaries of the Coach no more than three or four times a week. They stand resolute at the bar in their tweed jackets and improbable cravats, sipping their vodka and posing for photographs for tourists who can scarcely believe their luck in stumbling over this perfectly preserved slice of Old England.

"The country is trying on the nerves," says Rodney. "You and me cannot take it. You're never alone in the country. There is always some busybody, pestering you for your opinions on the weather or giving you advice on rhubarb.

"You have neighbours. In London, you also have neighbours, but they are invisible, too old or neurotic to bother your peace of mind. In the country, whatever their age or state of mind, they pry. They invite you to tea. They put your name down for local societies. They expect to see you in church.

"There is no breathing space in the country. For that, you need the peaceful anonymity of a great city."

Rodney finishes his third pint with the lack of fuss that comes with practice. He relapses into another silence. But quite as much as his long speeches, Rodney's silences need lubricating. I go to the bar.

Rodney is launching into a learned and improving discourse on the Barmaid in Literary History when our peaceful anonymity is rudely interrupted. As interrupters go, they don't come much ruder than the editorial staff on *Private Eye*.

They announce their arrival with a concerted tapping of index fingers on noses and significant glances in my direction. This is their discreet and friendly way of intimating that they are once again on the point of dragging the J reputation through the manure.

MARK JONES

The deputy editor, a tall young man with the red face of an expelled public schoolboy and the clothes of an unsuccessful bookmaker, comes over. He is called deputy editor because he is generally deputised to gloat on any victims that may be around. He shakes hands with the elaborate and florid charm that has led to his nose being broken more times than a scrum half's.

"We heard about the boardroom table affair, Mark," he says in a grave voice. "Very shocking. Not exactly discreet, my man. Far from discreet."

I look to Rodney for support, but he is looking the other way, upset that his discourse on literary barmaids has been interrupted.

"Tell me what the charge is."

The Deputy declaims the news with a broad grin and in a voice loud enough for the whole pub to hear.

"I am referring to intense discussions you held in the offices of a certain advertising agency recently with a young lady called Lori something. After lights out," he adds meaningly. "*On* the boardroom table," he continues, with even more innuendo to the inch.

"I see. It's futile asking you where you heard this because you won't tell me and, second, because I know already. But if you take Sally's word, you underestimate both of us."

"How?"

"You underestimate her inability to tell the truth and my ability to sue. I hate to spoil your story for you – honestly – but it simply is not true. Watch my lips. N-o-t t-r-u-e. Inaccurate. Misleading. Unequivocal denial couched in the strongest terms and all that."

"But you do know her."

"I know you, but we've never made love on a black ash table."

"Aha! So you remember what kind of table it was!"

"Come on, *all* advertising agencies have black ash tables."

The editor comes over and puts a restraining arm around his Deputy's throat.

"I'm sorry, sir, has this man been bothering you? We've had our eye on him for some time. Shady character."

It is one of life's bigger mysteries that the editor of *Private Eye* should be a gentleman, a charming host and a loyal friend. He is just the kind of person you'd like to introduce to your mother. You could introduce them in the confident knowledge that she would be thoroughly charmed by his bright, considerate manner. She might even want to know why more of your friends aren't like him. He would probably then go off and write a story linking your mother with Sir Geoffrey Howe or something. And if the story proved false, he would be sure to apologise in the fullest and most sincere way the next time they met.

We exchange friendly greetings, notwithstanding my urgent desire to throw him and his magazine into the nearest sewer.

Rodney now decides to snap out of his reverie.

"And what," he demands, "is wrong with having sexual intercourse on a boardroom table?"

"That's not the point, Rodney. The point is, I didn't."

He ignores me. As usual.

"Uncomfortable, perhaps. But people tell me that sex in uncomfortable places often adds to the thrill. Something about hard and soft textures, I think."

The *Eye* delegation exchange glances in a way that suggest they cannot believe their luck.

"But I fail to see," he continues, "what is morally reprehensible in the act. I assume that Mark and his friend had the courtesy to dust the table afterwards and left the office as they would wish to find it. I can't see why that should be of interest to a magazine."

"Well," says the Deputy, hardly knowing where to begin. "He's a journalist, always telling other people how to behave. The fact that he has been caught with his pants down and willy dangling like this is interesting, isn't it? *And* very funny."

"Why?"

"Well . . . two people in an ad agency at dead of night . . . on the boardroom table . . ." The *Eye* lot are having trouble breathing. "Humping . . ." Explosion of giggles. "*I* find it funny . . ."

"Did *you* find it funny at the time?"

"As I didn't do it, Rodney, I really can't say. If you were the girl, I suppose it might be funny. If you were a girl doing it with the Deputy I suppose you'd find it very funny indeed." The *Eyes* frown and tut-tut at each other. You are allowed to make jokes at their expense, but they have to be better than their own.

Rodney is coming back to his point.

"But there is nothing intrinsically funny in the act. Nor is Mark a figure of national importance, nor, despite what you say, a notorious cant merchant." More titters. "So I return to my original question: why write the thing?"

The editor takes over from the exasperated Deputy.

"Don't you think it's wrong that they used an advertising boardroom for sex?"

Rodney considers this.

"It is far better," he says firmly, "than using it for advertising."

*

An evening's drinking with Rodney is an intense and arduous business. We pass from bar to pub, Rodney looking uniquely out of place in a green tweed jacket, grey trousers and frayed shirt. The rubberneck men in their Armani and Commes des Garçons turn their sleek heads towards him, gaze sardonically for a second, then turn back and say something that makes their rubberneck girlfriends laugh. Again, I want to shake Rodney: "CAN'T YOU SEE THEM, DON'T YOU MIND OR ARE YOU JUST PRETENDING??"

I wish I could make even a convincing show of obliviousness. In the fashion wars, I am one of the conscripted ranks, trudging after the generals with muttered curses, despising and envying conscientious objectors like Rodney, the people who stayed at home and braved the ridicule. Fashion isn't just clothes: it's eating, drinking, talking and acting. It is what the style journalists call *attitude*. Attitude is jolting a stranger's elbow and not apologising. Attitude is setting fire to someone's hair when you're lighting a cigarette and saying "Hey! Punk! Get your derro hair *outa my match!*" Attitude is aristocratic and working class, Young Fogey and Hip-Hop, Chelsea and Brixton. Rodney has attitude in bags. He dares: dares to look as if he doesn't care, and perhaps he doesn't. Caring is written all over me. There is caring in the modified, cheaper copies of last year's Spring collections that I wear. Caring in the apology I make to the fashion victim who backed into me at the bar. Caring in the politics I learnt in the 1970s, politics as unfashionable as the clothes we kept on

61

wearing even after Punk and Thatcher had changed everything.

Finally, Rodney announces that our researches are at an end. "I think we may now safely go out and enjoy ourselves," he says, slamming down his empty whisky glass with an air of authority. "What is that hateful little dive you go to off Drury Lane?"

*

The hateful little dive in question is the Zanzibar Club. This is a perplexing joint; I am never sure whether it is wise to be spotted here. But they do serve alcohol until the early hours and there will be plenty of opportunities for Rodney, even if he is nominally there for pleasure alone, to do some work on another thesis, *The Bimbo in Late Twentieth Century Society*.

The Zanz is famous for being one of the first clubs for unclubbable people. Pop stars, admen, non-RADA actors, TV people all piled in and its success was instant. Equally instantaneous was its first period of being hilariously out of fashion, since which time it has swung with dizzying speed between the fairly cool and the utterly naff.

Fashion is the blessing and a curse for places such as the Zanzibar. Traditional clubs – that is, Gentlemen's clubs – are less influenced by its whims. This is probably just as well. Imagine the scene in the Garrick:

JUDGE: (gravely sips imported Czech Budweiser from the bottle) Do you know, I clocked Alec Guinness the other night. Out on a crack. And check this, comrade, he was going into *Boodle's!*
BISHOP: (spilling his San Miguel in shock) Get outa here!

JUDGE: No, we're talking a whole-and-nothing-but scenario here. Guinness was going into Boodles. I grabbed him by the arm, of course. "Yo! Alec, my man!" I say. "Surely not? *No one's* been to Boodle's since the Lovin' Spoonful were in the charts and we were all buying our psychedelic sock suspenders in Carnaby Street. Quite lively after Synod, granted, and the transsexual hip-hop disco on Monday night is a bit of a laugh, but it's *passé*, my dear misguided thespian, pass-é!"

BISHOP: (takes a conspiratorial swig) I do wonder about Alec. All that Catholic jive in his autobiography.

JUDGE: (in a low voice) So do I. And Catholicism, don't you think, is *so* old hat. Really 1930s.

Tonight, the Zanzibar seems to be free of judges and bishops. The place is tolerably swinging all the same.

We are shown to one of the club's skilfully-slashed banquettes (Teddy Boy Revival Night, 1987) by a waitress in the early stages of anorexia nervosa. We settle back comfortably and Rodney's face takes on that philosophical look known and feared by students and barmen throughout London.

A noisy party comes in. Leading the way is a baggy blue suit with a chat show host inside. It's JONATHAN ROSS, the world's most ephemeral person!

As he enters, the whole bar shouts JOHNNNYYYY!! MY MAAAAAAANNN! But only to themselves. Outwardly, they turn to their friends and speak earnestly, trying to look as if they couldn't care less that JOHNNNYYYY! is in their midst.

He is with a mixed group of a dozen bodies, none of them heavier than about nine stone and only a couple older than 19. They are celebrating his wife's birthday. On appearances alone, you suspect that her birthday still leaves her a couple of years short of the age of consent and you wonder what clever, Jerry Lee Lewis-like trick Johnny played to square it with the vicar.

Jonathan looks benignly around the room, as if seeking out his floor manager. I beam back. We did meet once at a party. I remember telling everyone afterwards that he wasn't the arrogant, talentless creep you'd take him for.

Jonathan beams again, but at his wife (who, admittedly, is well worth beaming at).

"SIMON DEE," I shout in Johnny's direction.

The decline and fall of Dee, the most ephemeral chat show host of the Sixties, usually acts like Kryptonite on Ross.

This time, he just looks startled; the bar staff just look angry.

"He's such an arrogant, talentless creep," I say to Rodney as the management persuades me to sit down.

"Who would that be now?" asks Rodney.

"It would take too long to explain and the minutes are precious. Have another burble?"

"If you mean bottle rather than burble, then yes. It would be unwise and possibly dangerous not to."

*

Looking at Johnny's friends, I feel like Darwin discovering a new subspecies.

The plumage is of the standard Soho variety. Black microskirts, black tights and big earrings for the girls; black turtle necks, black peg trousers and small earrings for the boys. Their faces are an anthropological revelation; to wit, their uniform blankness.

A few years ago, faces were worn taut and sulky. Now, the cry seems to be Less is More and Nothing is Even More. There is a set look about the Johnny gang, as if their expressions have been fixed with gel in the bathroom mirror. Someone smiles, and you half expect them to dash to the loo to reset the stray lip.

They are not drinking, or hardly at all. The girls have glasses of Perrier in champagne glasses. The boys manfully clutch bottles of Beck's, but the level doesn't seem to go down. The attendant waitress is underemployed. Fortunately, she also has Rodney and me to look after. Rodney asks if she has ever thought of writing a novel and she smiles.

I go to the gents'. In the mirror I try out a blank expression by arching my eyebrows and sucking in my cheeks. Unfortunately, the image in the mirror looks more like Gary Glitter after a facelift.

I splash cold water on my face, as well as on my shirt, tie, trousers, shoes and the floor. Drinking makes me look old. The high line where my cheekbones are supposed to be is plummeting south like a graph showing the trade deficit. Locks of the carefully plastered-back hair are sticking out at odd angles, which is useless unless the Stan Laurel look enjoys a revival. The nose looks big and squashy, the eyes are bloodshot.

The door opens and a young man in black comes in. I realise that I am leaning with my head against the mirror.

*

Back at the table, I am feeling about 42 years old. Rodney has entered his benign phase, arms resting comfortably on his belly, eyes resting fondly on the bottle of champagne: he looks 43.

"You're getting a receding hairline, you know."

Rodney clumsily feels his scalp and smiles a contented smile.

A thin, stockinged leg brushes past mine as a rather wonderful 16- or 17-year-old friend of Johnny's tries to squeeze past. I raise my left eyebrow in a look that is meant to combine curiosity, a sense of humour and immense erotic expertise all in one. She trips over the stool, revealing a demure pair of white Marks and Spencers briefs under her tights.

"Don't bother to move for me, *please*," she says, adding another five years to my age.

*

Johnny's party, as clear-headed as when they arrived, goes into the night. Rodney, meanwhile, is pouring again, gazing at the bottle as if it is a long-lost lover with whom he has just been reunited.

"Rodney. Do you think we drink too much?"

Rodney's face is beyond registering very much. This could be the mood of the place or it could be the drink. But he does manage a look of contempt.

*

It is well past 2.30 am when we step gingerly on to Great Queen Street, taking care that it doesn't move suddenly and catch us unawares. The Masonic temple towers above us at an angle of 70° while the moon races across the sky doing 80 mph. The light is theatrical: the temple and the houses are pieces of chipboard scenery ready to fall on us. I attempt a few Fred Astaire steps down the steps of the club, but it doesn't work very well.

Rodney stands on one foot in the gutter surveying the temple with a look of tense bemusement. We have had the Dry, the Argumentative, the Benign and the Blank; now he is entering the Belligerent Phase. If Rodney was an orchestral symphony, he would now be one of Brahms's noisier and more turbulent passages, all angst and swirling strings.

He wanders up to the door of the temple and bangs hard on it with his fists.

"FUCKING MASONS!" he shouts. "COME OUT YOU BASTARDS! HEATHENS! BASTARDS! POLICEMEN! I'LL HAVE YOU ALL!"

I watch his performance with the indifference of a man who is fully occupied with the job of staying upright. I try leaning against the lamp-post, the door of the club and finally discover a comfortable spot lying across the bonnet of a car. I have the odd feeling that there is an audience watching me, so I wave an arm just in case.

Having run out of insults, Rodney is standing in the middle of the road making violent v-signs at the temple and bellowing the word "YOOORRRRRR!"

We are in this picturesque situation when a police car draws up noiselessly. Two flatties get out.

"All right, lad, cool it," says one to Rodney, who ignores him.

The other heaves me up from the car bonnet and sets me on the pavement like a skittle.

"What's up with your mate?"

I think hard for an explanation other than Rodney's consumption of 20 times the recommended weekly intake of alcohol units for the average adult male.

"He seems to think that the temple threatened him. I think it called him a rude name." I collapse on the bonnet in giggles. This detracts from the eloquence of my explanation somewhat.

The moon keeps its spotlight on us as a dramatic scene unfolds.

(Flattie B crosses centre stage and joins Flattie A in laying restraining hand on Rodney. Rodney struggles.)

RODNEY: Just let me get at the bastards! The FILTHY HEATHEN BASTARDS!

FLATTIE B: Calm down, sonny. Just watch it. People are trying to sleep.

RODNEY: *(detaching himself, appeals tearfully)* But I'm acting in the best spirits of academic research. WHO WILL RID ME OF THESE PESTILENTIAL MASONS? *(turns to Flattie B)* Will you?

FLATTIE B: Listen, mate, you go home and sleep it off or you come with us, all right?

(As Rodney stares at him, a horrified look gradually crosses his face.)

RODNEY: Oh Jesus. You're feds. The filth. The black and tans. Fucking MASONS. Let's see your sodding trousers –"

(He falls to the ground and attempts to roll up the trouser leg of Flattie B. Flattie B and Flattie A crush him to the pavement.)

FLATTIE B: Little cunt!

(They bundle Rodney into the car. As they crumple him inside, his head cracks sickeningly against the roof. They slam the doors and drive off.)

*

The stage is empty, the audience has gone and I want to go home. The legs want to stay where they are, however, and what is left of my mind is trying to work out what is happening to Rodney in the police car.

A cab passes by. Fortunately, the mind and legs decide to act in concert so I jump up and down and wave my arms. The cab drives on, then, I suppose, changes his mind. He stops 50 yards down the road and I run after him, still waving.

The driver leans over, opens the window a mean three inches and pokes a mean three inches of face at me.

"You're not gonna throw up in the back of the cab, are you?"

I consider this for a second.

"I don't think so. But I may swear a lot."

"You'd better fucking not."

"What? Fucking swear or fucking throw up?"

He lets out an angry sigh.

"Where you going?"

"Heaven, I hope. Not like the Metropolitan Police Force. Nor you, by the look of it."

He swears – as he is in the front of the cab he's allowed to – and drives off. A lot of people seem to have driven off tonight and quite a few have sworn. Once again there is just me and the Masonic temple.

*

Once again, I have to walk, walk, walk. Only this time, London seems all right. I'll go further. London is beautiful. There is no traffic, not even irate taxis or masonic policemen.

The buildings are low and homely and there are trees above them.

A pastoral mood envelops me and I set off for the trees. I stride towards Lincoln's Inn Fields feeling like Wordsworth in the Lake District. Wordsworth's faculties were usually in better shape than mine at the present time, but then I'm not in love with my sister while having to live with my wife. So sucks to you, Wordsworth.

The air is warm and invigorating, there is a soft breeze in the trees etched against a deep blue sky and I am feeling exhilarated. Rodney's plight is a little worrying, but he is bound to put on his best lecturer's manner, bore them silly and be released promptly from his durance.

I put on a sprint, urging myself on with an internal running commentary. *And J's literally hurtling along . . . look at this boy's rhythm, his balance . . . ooh! he took that corner beautifully . . . the Zanzibar to Highbury Corner record must be in danger if this quite superb athlete keeps it up . . .*

Then I trip over an outstretched foot and tumble into someone's arms.

"God, sorry," I say as I grasp his leather jacket to stop myself falling. But then there is a leather sleeve around my throat and my arm is twisted cruelly behind my back. Someone else comes up and kicks my legs from under me and I am dragged to a dark spot by the railings.

"Sit the fucker down here."

They set me down quite gently. It crosses my mind that they are treating me like an invalid, like someone who has just fainted in the street. The calf muscle where they kicked me begins to ache.

They sit on either side of me, close, knowing I won't move.

"Come on, then," says the one on the right. He is a kid with white bleached hair and a mocking expression on his smooth face. He doesn't speak viciously, but with a kind of sarcastic malevolence that makes me feel stupid as well as hurt and frightened. The other one is a small Greek teenager with heavy doped-up eyes. He takes my tie, examines it and turns it over to look at the label. Then he pulls it tight against my neck.

The Zanzibar nearly cleaned me out. I pull a fiver out of my trouser pocket.

"That all, pretty boy?" says the Greek guy, pulling the tie so my lips are close to his. I can't speak; so I nod. Don't cry now, you wimp. Don't let them see you cry.

"Cards," says the one in the leather jacket. "Chequebook." I give them my wallet.

"*Chequebook*," says the Greek. He reaches roughly into my breast pocket and finds nothing. Again he checks the label.

"Stand up." They force me to my feet. The one in the leather jacket holds me around the waist, grinning now. The Greek eyes me up and down.

"Take off your jacket, scumbag." I take it off and hand it over. Don't make me strip. Please, don't make me strip.

The kid with the bleached hair comes around in front of me. With elaborate grace, he inches up my tie and dusts me down. I am trembling and my hair has fallen uncomfortably over my eyes. He pinches my cheek.

"All right, yuppy," he says softly. "On your way." I walk away. Then he kicks me hard in the small of the back. I run, run hard. They run after me. I run harder on the shadowy flagstones, alcohol frothing inside me, the pain of my calf muscle getting worse.

At the end of the square they let me go. But I keep running

until the stitch in my side makes me stop. Then I walk and jog, angry, crying, spitting, walk and jog until I reach home.

CHAPTER NINE

I n an impassioned speech, Mr Mark J today called for much tougher prison sentences for violent offenders. Mr J spoke out from his North London home, where he is recovering from an attack by two unidentified youths in the early hours of this morning.

He said that anyone convicted of mugging should be sentenced to life, preferably in ball and chains to stop them kicking people. He also appealed to the public to look out for a 5 ft 7 in man of Greek appearance wearing a Boss wool jacket with Paisley lining. He said that the man may be dangerous, but that members of the public should nevertheless approach him and "give him a good kick in the goolies with my blessing".

Mr J also joined in the growing wave of protest at the alleged mistreatment of Mr Rodney O'Connor after his arrest just before the mugging in the early hours of Wednesday morning.

O'Connor was released without charge after being detained overnight and immediately lodged a complaint about what he claims was the unnecessary force used by the arresting officers.

A doctor who examined O'Connor confirmed that he had sustained cuts, bruises "and the most spectacular hangover I have seen in all my years in the medical profession".

CHAPTER TEN

". . . Yes, sir, we've put a stop on the card. In future, we do advise you to take out one of our Card-secure insurance policies, however . . ."

"Yes, sir, we do have your description of the youths involved on file. We are doing all we can, yes. But incidents such as this *are* very common in the Central London area and our hands are very full at the moment. No, sir, that does not mean we are not trying . . ."

". . . If you look at the figures, you'll see that complaints about police brutality have dropped sharply of late. And I'm sorry, the Press Office cannot comment on your friend's case until it has been thoroughly investigated. Please call if we can be of any further assistance . . ."

". . . O'Connor the law-abiding, O'Connor the pacifist is no more. Enter O'Connor the crazed Irish radical dedicated to overthrowing the Imperialist British police state and combating masonic influence wherever it festers. What? What the hell does it matter that I was born in Liverpool? Isn't that Irish enough for you? All that matters is that O'Connor is on the warpath. The Easter Rising will seem like small beer by the time I've finished . . ."

". . . But Mark, it must have been *appalling*. Did you say they tried to strip you? Oh. Not really. That's all right then. God you're so brave. I'd have fainted. It's like a Charles Bronson film. Isn't London horrible?"

". . . I know, but you've got to stand up to these people, otherwise society just disintegrates. Anyway, these weirdos are all cowards. They don't expect you to fight back. Like the time that bloke tried to do me with a razor blade. I just told him to get stuffed, right?"

". . . Listen, Mark, I know how you're feeling. You're going to find it very hard to get over this. People do. Now I don't want to impose, honestly, but I'm happy to give you my analyst's number. He's very good, really. You remember when I was living with John and we were having all those sexual problems? Well, my analyst was marvellous then. And mugging, I don't know, it's such an *infringement*. You must feel dirty . . . infected. It's a sort of rape, really . . ."

". . . Mark, hello, it's me. I heard about your thingy from Soapy – he heard about it from Sally, they went out for a drink, isn't she a scream? God, that girl . . . Listen, it sounds really, really horrid. I mean, they should just be shot or something, shouldn't they? But listen, there is something I can do. You know that place in Fulham I was telling you about, and while I think about it, do tell me if you've got a lunch date free yet. Anyway, they also do self-defence courses. Brilliant, isn't it? There's a really good instructor, Barry, he used to be in the SAS or something like that. I went to one and it was *such* fun. Why don't I get you into a class? Gratis, *bien sûr*. There's a really good feature there . . ."

". . . Yeah, Lori heard about it. She was really upset, I think. Hasn't she 'phoned you yet? She said she would."

". . . It's Sally. I thought I'd better ring and do my Florence Nightingale bit. You poor darling. There you are, going on all the time about how misunderstood these thugs are, then the ungrateful brutes go and do this to you. It isn't fair. I hope you gave them a good talking-to. But to more important things: are you really moving to Abbeybrooke? I hear you had a lovely time down there with Soapy and his sister. Isn't she adorable? . . ."

". . . Listen, Mark, haven't got long, but the editor's really keen on a feature on mugging, how you feel afterwards, what you'd like to do to them if you ever caught up with them, all that. Can we talk? We need 1,000 words by Monday."

". . . Mark. This is Wendy. It's just terrible, terrible. I've been in tears virtually all morning. You *must* come round and talk. Please. I know you'll feel better if we talk. Please give me a ring. All my love . . ."

CHAPTER ELEVEN

Down a flight of steps in Notting Hill. On the window-sill there is a line of small spindly plants. Behind them, the view into the downstairs room is blocked by the kind of concertina metal gate you see on old lifts.

At the bottom, a bike is chained in three different places to the iron handrail. My shin crashes into the bike, I swear and walk to the door.

"WOR-WOR, WOR-WOR, WOR ... ARGGGGGHHHHH ... WOR WOR-WOR WOR!!!" The bark is that of a Rottweiler or some equally infernal hound: a snarling, rabid, depraved bark.

"Oh, shut up!" The barking stops in mid WOR! There is a pause, then the sound of about half a dozen bolts being drawn. The door opens on its chain and Wendy's nose appears.

"Oh, Mark, it's you. Thank God. Come in."

"Not until that dog is chained, muzzled or put to sleep I don't."

"Oh don't worry about him. He's harmless." She opens the door and ushers me in. "Come and say hello to Rotty. He won't bite, promise."

She is right: he won't bite. Rotty is a small loudspeaker with a plug attached.

"Lovely, isn't he? He's an alarm. You set the level to pick up noises outside and he barks, as loud as you want. He's very effective and you don't need to take him for walks."

"He's very realistic." Indeed he is. I wonder when Wendy last had any mail delivered.

"He doesn't need grooming or training."

"That's a matter of opinion."

Wendy is small and alert with a mass of curly red hair. The hair is so springy that, like the boy in *Cider with Rosie*, your first impulse is to hit her on the head with a stick to see what happens. But then you notice her challenging green eyes and have second thoughts. The eyes look like a combination of Becky Sharp and one of Edna O'Brien's less shrinking heroines. You can easily imagine her laying out a drunken Irish seducer with a single blow of her small fist.

All of which is rather misleading. For by profession Wendy is a publisher of children's books, and one of the less aggressive examples of a breed not noted for their aggression. But the green eyes aren't there for nothing; if pushed hard enough, she has a bite, if not like a Rottweiler, then at least like a bad-tempered Pekinese. Many a complacent male author venturing tales of roguish little boys and curly-haired girlies has left her office suffering from a sore ankle or a throbbing ear.

Wendy is extremely nervous of intruders. The front door is

a recreation ground for locksmiths. The windows are Chubb-locked, barred and alarmed. Also alarming is the atmosphere in the flat, heavy with pot-pourri and the lack of ventilation. It is a good thing that Rotty isn't a real dog because he would be too drugged and drowsy to present a real threat to any bur-glar. As it is, the loudspeaker Rotty is the only thing in the flat with a clear head.

Wendy bustles around in the kitchen and threatens to in-flict herbal tea on me.

"Oh God," she says, tugging a handful of hair in self-reproach. "I suppose you'll want something stronger after what you've been through."

Does she mean tap water?

"I've got some gin somewhere."

"I've managed to get through twenty-eight years without drinking gin at eleven in the morning, so I'll last a bit longer. Coffee will do fine. My nerves aren't that bad."

"If you're sure."

"Losing your wallet doesn't immediately turn you to drink. Not unless the guys who stole it decide to start shop-ping at Joseph and Ralph Lauren."

We are seated in the stripped pine, Liberty-patterned living room. At least, I am seated; Wendy is perched on a kitchen stool, her eyes turned pityingly on me.

"You must be a wreck."

I examine my clothes, offended.

"No, not the way you look. How stupid. Sorry. Oh, but you're probably teasing, aren't you? Okay. No, you know what I mean. I'm amazed you can go outside again at night. You're being very brave."

I wasn't at all brave; I was bricking myself, and I should tell her so. I ran, I wept. Why, then, can't I tell her so?

"It's not bravery, Wendy. It's just one of those things that happen in cities. You cope."

"Well, I don't think I could, and I *still* think you're very brave. How could you stand up to those people without caving in?"

This is becoming uncomfortable.

"I suppose it's just shock or something. You feel quite calm, somehow." *I wish I could stop doing this.* "I suppose if you did cave in they'd make it twice as bad for you."

"How could it have been worse?" Wendy's eyes are filling with tears. This is horrible.

"They might have killed me." *Damn. Over-dramatising as well.*

"Or hurt me, or done anything."

"But they *did* hurt you," she wails.

"Yes, well, I suppose they did a bit." *Next, I'll be saying it's just a scratch.* "It's nothing, really. Just a kick."

She continues to gawp at me.

"Perhaps you should see a doctor. Have you been – hush!" Wendy tenses. Footsteps that were clattering on the pavement above our heads suddenly stop. Wendy tenses and her eyes roll towards the window. There is a shuffling. Then the footsteps continue, away down the road. She relaxes. I begin to feel depressed.

"Anyway, Mark, I'm so glad you came over. I mean, I think you should be with someone at a time like this."

"How do you mean?"

She takes a deep breath.

"I've been thinking about you, and the way you live. And, I know this sounds funny, but I really think it has something to do with what happened to you the other night."

"You lost me there."

She does some more fierce hair tugging. Luckily, the stuff has the resilience of steel wool.

"You *do* know what I mean. The way you run your life. Going out with different women, going to all those parties, ogling at famous people, trying to live like them . . . not *settling*. Drinking a lot. God, I don't want to sound like your mother, but you really should have a good look at yourself. You throw away your intelligence and niceness on these jibes and one-liners all the time."

I wasn't feeling particularly down before. I might be soon if this goes on.

"A mugging isn't going to stop me going out at night, if that's what you mean."

"Of course it's not," she says with a touch of exasperation. "Just try not to be so male and self-protective all the time. Are you in a relationship?"

"I'm in several."

"You know what I mean. Mark, PLEASE don't be so confrontational. I am trying to help. I know the way you live your life and it isn't healthy. You're so vulnerable. You can't get around every situation with just your own self-esteem to carry you through. I can see you now striding home, all drunk and self-important, then these people do this to you. There's got to be a lesson in it somewhere."

She pulls her hair tight back from her forehead. "You've got to have some security. You're very insecure."

I take in the flowery curtains, the iron bars on the windows, the jars of pot-pourri, the locks, the soft cushions that envelop my shoulders. Rotty is keeping a watchful eye on me in the corner.

"Security can be inhibiting."

"What rubbish, Mark. With another person you've got a

defence against the world. You're safer. In all sorts of ways. God, just look at London. Infections, violence, diseases . . . it's horrible facing all that alone."

For the first time since I arrived, I think of Wendy instead of myself. Of her kindness, and her intelligence and her deep, serious expression inviting you to tease, and her lovely eyes.

I sigh deeply and glance out of the window.

"I'm unsettled, Wendy. I can't settle down when I'm unsettled."

She gets up, then sits astride a dining-room chair.

"You're making others unsettled too, you know." She suddenly looks stern. "I read about your unsettled behaviour in *Private Eye*."

That is one of those phrases that make your mouth dry up. Like "will you just pull over to the side, sir," or "I'm ringing from Extortion and Writ, solicitors, with regard to an article that appeared in your column yesterday."

"What?"

"I don't remember. But it was very sordid. Something about two girls." She gets up and goes to the kitchen.

"It may not be true, of course," I call after her.

After a moment, she comes back.

"It just made me really sad."

"Don't tell me. And disappointed. But I really don't know what they're going on about."

"It's enough that someone should think that it's true, isn't it?"

*

I pat Rotty warily as she unbolts the bolts and unlocks the locks.

"Mark. I'm sorry I went on at you. You know what I'm like."

We fall into each other's arms, and hug tightly, my face deep in her hair. I squeeze her urgently and she responds. We stand like this for a long time, swaying gently together.

"Wendy," I say, through the curtain of thick hair. "Let's make love together."

She sighs and pushes me gently away. Her mouth is a twisted regretful line.

"No, Mark. Not until you've sorted yourself out." She takes me by the hand, squeezes it tight, then lets it fall from her hand.

"Let's go and lie down together," she says finally. "Just so we can feel each other there."

I nearly say, "feel each other where?", but stop myself just in time. We go to the bedroom, leaving the door unbolted.

CHAPTER TWELVE

The energy and dedication of fearless investigative journalist Mark J knows no bounds. The dashing young sleuth has been squiring not one but two media lovelies of late.

Media lovely number one is Sally Bretforton, pin-up girl of half the City of London, half the Palace of Westminster (the Conservative side) and a long-time associate of the disgusting J. J has been heard loudly boasting that Ms Bretforton is "besotted" with him, a claim that almost led to fisticuffs between himself and sottish estate agent Soapy Cox in a Wiltshire pub recently.

Media lovely number two is Lori Cartwright, an ad agency bimbo with whom J has been spotted in several intense, late-night meetings. One of these took place in the boardroom of her own agency and was held, eccentrically enough, in total darkness.

The libidinous J's fleetness of foot will be needed more

than ever in the coming weeks. It seems only a matter of time before the source of his over-activity is done permanent damage, either by one of the rivals or their several legions of admirers.

CHAPTER THIRTEEN

"Hi, Mark, it's Grizz. You all right, then?"

"Not bad."

"Thought I'd give you a bell. I'm down in the Smoke on Friday."

"Fine. Let's go for a drink."

"What a clever chap you are. Which pub?"

"How about Soho?"

"You dirty bastard."

"I belong to this really sleazy club in Dean Street we could go to. The Groucho Club Erotica."

"You're pissing about. I'm not going to some bloody strip joint."

"Honestly, it's a really classy place. Great floorshow."

"Five quid for a half of pissy lager."

"No, £2.50 for a bottle of obscure Eastern European beer."

*

I inspect my clothes in the windows of Charing Cross Road and try to examine the feelings about meeting Old School Buddy Grizz that lie underneath them. Lovely to see this relic of lost youth and all that: one just hopes that the relic has had a haircut, shaved off its beard and realised that there are more types of natural fibre than a leather motorcycle jacket.

Walking past the long window, I catch the tilted chin, the supercilious look, the self-importance in my very walk. What a loathsome picture: successful, metropolitan Mark on his way to a night's patronising. Mark, the spoilt boy of the block showing off his new shoes and new, clipped accent. Mark the rubberneck, showing off his famous acquaintances.

And if Sally could share those thoughts with me, she'd doubtless add "Mark the poor, lost little self-torturing lad who has such a miserable time with these smooth-talking Southern folk. What he wants is an honest pint and a game of arrows with the lads." Then she would laugh rather a lot.

Grizz is waiting in the lobby of the Groucho gazing critically at a copy of *Harper's and Queen* when I arrive. He is wearing a polyester, narrow-lapelled but in the circumstances acceptable grey suit. The beard is still there, but the thick, dark hair only just covers his ears. Good. With any luck, people will think I'm taking my accountant out for a meal.

"I thought you was joking when you said this were a strip club."

"I were – I mean I was. Ah. I see what you mean." I follow his amused gaze towards a woman wearing a dress so figure-hugging that you expect to hear the figure gasping for breath.

"Nun's habits are being worn tight this season. Let's go in."

The Groucho Club bar is one of the sacred temples of the

rubberneck faith. The unclean and the incurious alike are forbidden to enter.

The celebrants all make the ritual turn of the neck as you enter; they size you up and decide immediately where, novice, priest or deity, you fit in the celebrity hierarchy. We stand on the threshold doing some neck craning of our own. Melvyn Bragg passes by and gives me an uncertain nod. This is a great sign of favouritism from one of the High Priests; we only met once, for five minutes at a party, a five minutes spent on my part explaining the mitigating circumstances surrounding a cheeky article I'd written about him. Grovelling, in other words. Grizz nudges me and points to Mel Smith telling jokes in a corner. Mel's friends look at Grizz disdainfully, and I gently explain that to point at a celebrity in the Groucho is like a Muslim facing West at prayers.

I install Grizz in one of the sofas that old Groucho lags always offer their guests. The guest sinks into its marshmallow cushions, so restricting movement and allowing the host (who has cannily placed himself on a firm armchair opposite) to make all the intelligent, animated gestures.

I make an intelligent gesture towards the waiter now, a frown, encouraging nod and slight drinking movement all in one. Blind to the considerable artistic skill so demonstrated, he ignores me and goes next door. Another waiter notices my less subtle and distinctly less cool wave; then he too forgets and also goes elsewhere. After three or four minutes, a waitress finally notices me kneeling on my chair, blushing and waving frantically.

"I thought you were being served. Sorry."

Grizz is half-submerged in the sofa, the shoulders of his jacket riding up around the neck and the look of a satisfied tourist on his face. We run through the news schedule. Sarah and John are back together. Soggy's gone back to Leeds. Mick was busted for the second time. Griff and Honda had a party, Sue and Moony are having a baby. At the Blue Anchor, the Red Cow and the Dog and Trumpet, things go on much as normal.

In my turn, I give up-to-date details of people Grizz has never heard of, places he's never been and scandals he couldn't care less about.

This doesn't take long. We lapse into a thoughtful silence, Grizz gazing south-west towards Mel Smith's table, me gazing north-east towards the door. I steal a glance at my watch: 8.45. And Grizz has already eaten, so I can't even introduce a spot of stage business in the form of a meal.

9.10 and, slowcoach, I am only now realising that Grizz's conversation is impeded by something more powerful than Czech lager. His pupils are dilated and his voice has that familiar, detached *timbre*.

I wouldn't mind, but Grizz is not *fashionably* stoned. He isn't part of the hip-hop druggie club; he doesn't get stoned so that he can keep dancing and going full tilt until the morning or until his internal organs cease to share the brain's expansionist vision and pack up altogether. Grizz gets stoned indoors, when everywhere is closed and he is alone with his Inner Circle. Grizz's style is torn-up cigarette packets and stuff that looks like sheep droppings in cellophane rolled up on an old Emerson, Lake and Palmer album. Grizz is decaying rooms with Indian tapestries and joss sticks. Grizz's people lie back on the old, damp sofa with dilated pupils and claim to see scenes from *Lord of the Rings*. Grizz's people break into meaningless laughter and use words that somehow escaped the mass extermination of all phrases invented in late 1960s San Francisco.

To do him justice, Grizz doesn't need drugs to talk spectacular piffle. He begins to expound one of those theories that makes Erich von Danniken's stories of biblical spaceman sound like the essence of exegetic caution.

"All the most amazing people in the planet's history, all the really famous people, have been sort of touched by something outside themselves," he says. "Basically, it's energy from somewhere else, isn't it? Not of this world."

"Not the Divine Flame story? Really Grizz, this is old hat. I'm surprised at you."

"Divine, but none of that Christian stuff. You're switched to this sceptical mode because you've not been chosen. Sorry. I don't want to freak you out, I mean, very few people are. You're not illuminati. I mean, Jesus had that Outside Energy, but so did others, like Buddha and Julius Caesar . . . and writers as well. Shakespeare and Tolkien."

"And Mel Smith?"

"Why not? I know you're being sarcastic, but why not? He's really good, I think. Did you see that sketch he did in the gents' loo that time with the hand dryer? Brilliant. Python definitely had it, and the Marx Brothers."

"So where does this Outside Energy come from? How do you spot someone with this extra-terrestrial virus?"

"They're sort of serene. They're above the things people usually worry about, like money and appearance and things like that."

"I'm sorry, but all the famous people I know care more about the way they look than anyone."

". . . they have this aura. Most people think the aura is something you can't touch and can't see. But you can if you're *touché*."

"If you're what?"

"*Touché*. I've just read this amazing book about the French Illuminati of the fourteenth century. They were known as the *touché*. You have it within you. It's like karma. Sometimes you can reach it through an out-of-body experience or an acid trip or something."

"What are the symptoms? Do you fly out of the window or something?"

Grizz is very patient with me. He leans forward and lays his palms fanned out a couple of inches above my head and moves them in a circular motion. I look around uneasily. I might have got away with the accountant story so far, but no longer. What would Rodney do in my place?

"See, you've got a really negative aura. All hostility and tightness."

"I must stop using the firm-hold gel."

"You don't have the Serenity." There is not much I can say to this; serene is the last thing I feel. "I'm trying to feel your sex waves."

"Keep your voice down, Grizz. What are they?"

"Sex waves? Self-explanatory. Great people have deeper, smoother sex waves. That's why they're so attractive to normal people. That's why they call Marilyn a Goddess."

"You're surely not going to tell me that Marilyn Monroe was a being from another planet? That beats the theory that she was bumped off by the CIA hands down. Can I be your literary agent?"

Grizz withdraws his hands and smiles serenely.

"And anyway," I insist, "she had a lousy sex life."

"That doesn't matter."

"It did to her."

Grizz's spot of hocus pocus has not gone unnoticed. Mel

Smith is looking over quizzically and any second now we are going to be snapped up to play two wallies in a BBC2 sketch.

"I see."

Grizz knows how much I am suffering, but refuses to let me off the hook.

"I believe I'm here for a purpose. I don't know what it is yet. But according to that book about the *touché*, a group of humanoids will make themselves known in the year 2000 and Explain Many Things."

Explain Many Things. With each enunciated capital letter my guts tighten another hilarious turn. Mel has got his group in stitches and it isn't hard to Explain Why. One last attempt before I give in.

"It's not unusual for people to feel that they've been called to some higher mission, Grizz," I explain, kindly. "There was Joanna Southcott, the farmer's daughter who thought she was going to give birth to the second Messiah at the beginning of the nineteenth century . . ."

"You don't need to show off in front of me, Mark. All this stuff just confuses you. I don't expect you to Believe. You'll see, all in good time."

"Come on, Grizz, this is silly. All this Illuminati stuff belongs in the 70s with concept albums and drum solos."

He continues to smile.

"Mark, for someone who went to university and all that, you've got a really narrow mind sometimes. All this stuff about 'the Seventies' and 'the Eighties', do you think it really matters when we're talking about the Timeless? . . . You're so, I don't know, *clogged up* with London and money, being smart and clever and all that – why don't you let yourself believe in something?"

He is sitting back, now almost completely enveloped by

the sofa. His hands are clasped, his chin tilted and there is a suspiciously evangelical look in his eyes.

"Grizz. Tell me the truth. Are you *touché?*"

His bleary eyes focus on mine and I get the beatific smile again.

"You won't understand if I tell you, Mark. But I don't mind you knowing. I am a sort of prophet."

An agonising spasm of laughter shoots through me. I stare intently at the floor.

*

I reknot my tie in the mirror of the gents' loo and summon up the energy to face another bout with the Infinite upstairs. I left Grizz communing with his aura, an aura made up in equal parts of supernatural wisdom and the static electricity from his Burton's suit. I just hope that he hasn't begun to Explain Many Things to anyone I know.

A shuffling sound comes from the cubicle, which isn't quite the sound that should be coming from the cubicle. I pay little heed to it, however, as I am trying once again to find out what happened to my cheekbones, and that requires concentration.

I quickly run through expressions A, B and C in the mirror (the 'mean', the 'moody' and the 'magnificent'). I seem to have lost ten years from my age since the night at the Zanzibar, but I am not averse to shedding a few more. Then the cubicle door opens and a woman walks out.

She is in her teens, has dishevelled short hair, a defiant and doped-up expression, a cotton skirt unbuttoned at the front and a silk shirt unbuttoned in most places, revealing a small white breast. A normal sort of breast – not something to go all Henry Miller over – but still a surprising thing to encounter in the gents' loo of the Groucho.

Her cheeks are the peach colour of a Renoir model, but this is the blush of sexual excitement rather than ashamed womanhood. Then the source of the sexual excitement appears: a boy of her own age with dark curly hair, sideboards, Paisley shirt, 501s more or less intact and a blush of the conventional variety. Neither of them look at me as they go out, even though I say "Good evening" with what in the circumstances is exemplary politeness.

Upstairs, there is something of a commotion. The girl behind the counter is nervously chewing bits of hair and fingernails – her own – and looking powerless. No wonder. She would need to be a good ten stone heavier to cope with the large bald man in the double-breasted suit who starts shouting at the girl from the gents' as she emerges. He grips her by the shirt, so imperilling the remaining buttons.

"You fucking slag!" he screams. She looks bored.

Like a fool, I try to calm things down. Like a fool, the manager tries to restore order. Like a sensible chap, the boy from the gents' is nowhere to be seen.

The inevitable happens. The bald guy swings at me with lousy timing and misses. I knee him reproachfully in the groin. Between us, the manager, a barman and myself bundle him outside on to the pavement. We grip him with the clumsiness of people unused to this kind of work. The Groucho is not a place that normally has to employ an ex-SAS man in a dinner jacket on the door. The bald man swears a good deal. We release him, having made him promise not to come inside again. He paces up and down, swearing a good deal more. Then he sees two policemen watching the scene with professional interest.

"Shit," he says, and kicks the wall of the club, which doesn't take any notice. Casting another look at the policemen, who by now are looking very interested, he storms off into the night.

Inside, the girl from the gents' is sitting across the arm of the sofa. The receptionist gently lays her coat on her lap and gives her a concerned look. The girl falls backwards over the arm on to the sofa and lies there staring at the ceiling, her feet kicking slightly.

*

"Why do people get so screwed up about sex?" asks Grizz when I tell him about the excitement in the lobby and the even greater excitement in the loo. "It's the first thing in my Charter. Be Free. Don't Hide."

"I think those two felt pretty free and they certainly didn't hide it very well."

"No, whatever you say, the sex aura around here is pretty unhealthy."

"I did tell you I was joking about the Club Erotica bit, didn't I?"

"Sure, and about Soho being taken over by yuppies and them closing all the sex shops and everything. I hear what you're saying. But you don't get rid of a place's aura just like that. It's still here. You can see it in people's faces. There's something hungry in them, you know what I mean? That's bad sex."

I follow his gaze around the club, which is full and still edgy after the lobby incident. Through the doors, I can see the manager talking urgently to a customer and the customer is shaking his head.

"I don't know," I say, trying to lighten things a little. "I could have some very agreeable sex with some of the women in here."

Grizz looks hard at me.

"Do you remember the cinema?"

"I do, Grizz, and I don't want to. You mean the *Emmannuelle* film."

"That was the sex aura. Violence. Hatred. Contempt. That was Soho. That's the kind of evil hunger you get around here."

"Listen, Grizz, be a mate. Drop the subject."

"I just hope you haven't been infected with it. God, I remember the state you were in that day. I remember you saying that you'd never set foot in London again, let alone Soho. I remember you said you was going to live in the country for good."

"All right, Grizz. It was a long time ago. People change. Places change. London isn't so bad."

"Do you still see Lorraine? She's in the Smoke now, you know."

I knew it was a mistake seeing Grizz tonight. He keeps those heavy, undeterred eyes on me and waits quietly for an answer.

"Yes, Lorraine's down here. Only she's not Lorraine anymore. She is now a very attractive, very outgoing and slightly neurotic woman who works for an advertising agency. She is now Lori."

CHAPTER FOURTEEN

Mr Mark J has finally broken his silence on the issue of his relations with Ms Lori Cartwright. Speculation about those relations, past and present, has reached fever pitch since Mr David Grisley raised the matter in the Groucho Club, London W1.

Mr J issued the following press statement:

"Lately there has been a great deal of speculation, much of it misinformed and mischievous, about Ms Cartwright and myself. I hope that the following statement will put an end to such speculation about what is, after all, a private matter. I also trust that Ms Cartwright, who is not known for her discretion, will have the sense to keep her trap shut.

"I have known Ms Cartwright since she was sixteen and I was seventeen. At that time, we went out together for six months and it was, considering the tenderness of our years, an extremely passionate attachment.

"The relationship was terminated after an incident in the cinema, an incident on which, for her sake, I have no wish to dwell. Would that the opposition parties had shown the same restraint.

"We were on distant terms for the remainder of our school-days. At eighteen, I went to university. A year later, Ms Cartwright emigrated to Los Angeles. I have no comment to make on rumours that she 'shacked up with a rich dopehead record producer'. That is her business, not mine.

"Some months ago, Ms Cartwright returned to London and took up a job with an advertising agency. In April, we met at a party in Soho. We have seen each other several times since then. That concludes my statement."

Mr J was besieged by further enquiries, such as "Do you still love her," "Is she the only floppy disk in your drive?" and "What about Sally?" But he offered no further comment.

CHAPTER FIFTEEN

Tristram spins around the dance floor, long coat tails and long hair (which, even under the lights, has a distinct *soupçon* of green at the sides) swirling around him.

The woman he is dancing with is obviously trying to look like Elizabeth Taylor. She has a lovely face, although there is rather a lot of it for my taste and it is plastered in white foundation which make the three beauty spots and bright turquoise lipstick stand out all the more. Her bright pink taffeta gown is full to overflowing and there are two obvious places where the dam is about to burst. In his frock coat and tight black trousers, skinny Tristram looks more than ordinarily like Uriah Heep.

The song playing is that one with the synthesised drum beat that goes *pop-pop-ker-push, pop-pop-ker-push*; that is, any one of the 200 different songs currently playing in London clubs under the soubriquets of House, Garage, New Jersey or

Belgian New Beat. Oblivious to the rhythm, Tristram and his friend pirouette around the floor like extras from *Amadeus*.

The song comes to an end, or rather it merges into a record the DJ assures us is the next crucial thing. This also goes *pop-pop-ker-push*, *pop-pop-ker-push*.

Having successfully brought a touch of elegance and beauty to the proceedings, Tristram kisses his partner's gloved hand; she curtsies, putting further pressure on the straining dam of taffeta. He comes over to me mopping his brow with a handkerchief which is half pink polka dot and half green Paisley.

"As I was saying," he says on reaching me. "This girl of yours, the Groucho knee trembler one, is an overnight star. There is a price on her head. No kidding. I've been trying to get hold of her all day."

"Does she *do* anything?"

"Who cares? Models. Dances, maybe. Sings, anyone can do that. Doesn't matter. She can do what she likes now she's cracked it with the tabloids."

"Tristram, all she's done so far is to screw someone in the loos of a club."

"ALL? It was a stroke of genius, my man. That girl is touched by the divine flame. You don't need any special talent to become famous; you or me could do it, if only we had the nerve – *or* the right guy behind us. Take this girl: there's someone who used what talent she had to the full. And what talent was that? Money, family and sex appeal. Daughter of wealthy military family bonks politician's son in top people's nightspot. Have you *seen* the papers today? They've all run something about it, or just about all. There's media exploitation for you."

"I know. I did the exploiting. Who do you think gave them the story?"

"You did, and very craftily done too, *mon brave*. Kept yourself out of it as well, didn't you, even though it was you who did the GBH on the Sugar Daddy when he cut up rough. Still, if you're serious about this exploiting business, you've got to go further."

"How?"

"You should've signed her up, my boy. On the spot. Got in there with a contract. This girl, believe me, is going to be the next Erica Rowe."

I let pass the obvious slight to my journalistic integrity. You have to let a lot of things pass with Tristram and integrity is principal among them.

"This is charming, my dear, but I can hardly hear you speak," Tristram calls over the 12-minute synthesised drum solo. "Let's go upstairs to the members' room."

We are in church. It is a deconsecrated church, which is just as well as its name is the Limelight Club, the decibel level is around a hundred times that produced by the lungs of the average congregation and the light show is definitely not the work of an inventive deacon with a couple of candles. The searchlights cast giant shadows of the heathen's ritualistic dance on the Gothic walls; the whole scene could be a Hollywood re-creation of the big party the Philistines had before Samson brought the roof down.

The Limelight's new management took a strong low-church line with some of the more flamboyant aspects of services at the club; and certainly in the old days some of the heathen used a wide variety of substances to work themselves up into a state of spiritual ecstasy. The place was revamped, narcotic smells were sniffed out and stamped on and they installed a posh members' bar in the upstairs vestry. We install ourselves there in our turn and Tristram orders two glasses of strange green champagne.

As usual, he has about a dozen schemes of varying respectability and chances of financial survival to tell me about.

The first stunt is a big celebrity ball, details of which he is prepared to give me on a cast-iron, exclusive, for-your-ears-only basis. This is an honour; and although it's one I will doubtless be sharing with about another dozen journalists, I thank him handsomely.

At the time of going to press, he tells me, there are a good 20 'D' celebs lined up; five or six Cs; the same number of Bs; and almost certainly an A.

The A is big news. Tristram, a conscientious man when it comes to rubbernecking, seldom awards A status to the famous freeloaders he invites to his parties. Ds are easy: just trawl through the cast of EastEnders and whatever show is appearing at the Palladium. Lyndsey de Paul and any other pop stars who have managed to remain photogenic despite not having had any hits in the past ten years will also do. Cs: stars of situation comedies, pop stars of the more ephemeral kind and aristocrats who have yet to be involved in a drugs or sex scandal. Bs are harder to come by. They include the likes of Michael Caine, George Michael, Bob Geldof and members of the higher and the disgraced ranks of the aristocracy. The A category is reserved for Royals and Elizabeth Taylor.

So the A is big news. He won't say which A it is, so I call him a liar and an incorrigible hype merchant. He thanks me, and we leave it at that.

"Now, to more important matters," he says. "Whom will the Randy Sleuth be escorting to this world-shattering event?"

"If you mean me, then no comment. Talk to my lawyers."

"I must congratulate you on getting that piece in *Private Eye*, by the way. That must have put a few grand on the yearly income."

"Don't congratulate me. Believe it or not, I didn't plant the story and furthermore it isn't true. In fact, I was rather upset about it."

Tristram is outraged.

"WHAT? Come on, Mark, these people are working for you. They've made you into good copy."

"All the same, I prefer to remain a humble reporter dedicated to my simple, unglamorous craft."

"Bullshit. You lot are only in it for the sex and the glamour and you know it."

"And you?"

"*Of course* I'm in it for the sex and the glamour dear boy, and thank God – sorry Sir, I know this is your House, didn't mean to swear – thankfully I admit it, unlike some people. Which brings me on to my other venture. The Rubbernecks' Club."

"The what?"

"I've had this idea. A club solely for rubbernecks and their victims. No pretence to be anything else, like the Groucho. Just good, old-fashioned ogling and star fucking.

"What you do is offer free membership to maybe 300, 350 hand-picked celebs. You get maybe half of those. Everyone else pays. So, natch, the celebs come along 'cause it's free and plebs like you pay to see the celebs. Brilliant, isn't it?"

"It sounds ghastly. Who is putting up the money, given that you're always one step ahead of the Official Receiver?"

"I'm doing very well, actually, so there. One or two cash flow problems, nothing more. But the money from this is coming from a mate who runs another club out Kensington way. Which reminds me, I want you to meet him."

This is awkward. Most of Tristram's club-owning friends are homicidal wide boys who are either just out of prison or are being kept out by the good offices of friendly CID men. Their clubs are places that neither your vicar nor your life insurance adviser would recommend you to visit – even if, as Tristram puts it, you can be sure of "a frigging good time".

"Who is he?"

"Evil Billy."

"Come on, Tristram, no one is called Evil Billy. You'll be telling me he wears a Zoot suit and carries a submachine gun next."

"Straight up. He's a top-notch man is Billy. Bent, and all that – has these cute punky boys in tight white shorts do the serving – but a fine man. Let me tell you what he did the last time I went to his place."

"Go on. I left my disbelief suspended in the cloakroom."

"Well, Billy knows which way I swing, so he puts on a special show for me. 'You come up here, Tristy,' he says. 'I've got just the fing for a dirty little sod like you.' So we go up to this small attic room where there's a DJ playing this really sultry music. And, I kid you not, there are six or seven *gorgeous* women there dancing together.

"But when I say women I'm exaggerating. A couple of them couldn't have been over thirteen or fourteen. They were mostly around sixteen, I guess, and they're *all* dressed in these really tight leather and rubber outfits.

"Anyway, Billy and me sit down – he's grinning all over his face – and these girls come over and start doing the act right in front of us. Rubbing up against each other, stroking each other, all that. I mean, I'm sitting there thinking that this is every man's sexual fantasy come true. The horniest thing I have ever seen."

"There must have been some anxious mothers in the East End that night."

"No, that's just it. These girls were as Sloaney as you like. Real class acts. I only recognised one – Charlie Pear-Samways's kid sister – but you could tell they were all as plummy as you like. They were just there for a laugh. God knows where Billy found them. But there they were, playing with their nubile little bodies, driving these really hard East End nuts mad. The girls were loving it."

"Did you offer to dance with any of them?"

"Well, Mark, to tell you the truth, the thought did cross my mind. I asked Billy if I could but he said he'd stuff my bollocks down my throat if I tried. 'Precious goods there, Tristy,' he says. 'Handle with care.' "

I absorb his story in silence.

"You're looking very thoughtful," he says.

"Tell me, isn't old Pear-Samways something big in the judiciary?"

CHAPTER SIXTEEN

"The Press Council has ruled that an article by Mr Mark J in *The Sunday Rubberneck* was indecent, highly offensive and unfounded in fact. The Council found that Mr J was unable to bring forward any witnesses or direct evidence to substantiate the story headlined 'Rubber-dub-dub! Toff girls in club orgy' dealing with events which allegedly took place at an establishment called 'Evil Billy's'. Moreover, the attempt to implicate Miss Emma Pear-Samways in this lurid account was both puerile and, potentially, deeply harmful to a young lady of Miss Pear-Samways's age. We can only hope that *The Sunday Rubberneck's* scurrilous and disagreeable article does not cause any lasting damage to her character."

CHAPTER SEVENTEEN

Another gents' loo: this time the one at the Ritz, where there are no semi-clothed army officers' daughters to be seen. But almost as intimidating is the presence of the worthy retainer who stands about two feet behind you as you pee, equipped with hair brushes, towels, and other items for spicking and spanning the well-heeled male. He is the kind of chirpy, respectful chappie who used to appear in English films of the 1940s. It is a harmless conceit of mine to think of him as a batman preparing the officers for the trenches.

BATMAN: Planning a little sortie, tonight, sir?
MAJOR J: Yes, Malin, there's a spot of bother brewing up the road at the Arts Club. We've a party ready to move in at 22 hundred hours.
BATMAN: Still a few skirmishes to sort out hereabouts first, sir.

MAJOR J: How d'yer mean?

BATMAN: Party of Hun businessmen, sir. In the conference room.

MAJOR J: Damn. Ugly bunch, I'll bet.

BATMAN: Pharmaceuticals company, sir, I believe.

MAJOR J: Chemical warfare bods, eh? The swine.

BATMAN: What's more, sir, there's still a battalion of Japs camped around the NAAFI.

MAJOR J: Looks like being a charming evening. Well, we'll give 'em a bit more than soy sauce and sushi to think about, Malin.

BATMAN: Ha, ha, sir.

MAJOR J: (finishes adjustments to battledress as Malin solicitously brushes his shoulder) By the way, Malin, if you see O'Connor's man, have a quiet word with him about the Major's turnout, will you?

BATMAN: (lowers voice discreetly) Major O'Connor a bit on the fusty side again, is he, sir?

MAJOR J: To say the least, Malin, to say the least. Well, here goes. Toodle-oo!

BATMAN: Good luck, sir.

Rodney is waiting for me in the lobby. He is indeed a little fusty. His dinner jacket, hardly the last word in chic in 1956, the year of its manufacture, looks like something all but the least fastidious jumble sale would turn down. The shirt failed the window test several years ago, the hair is disordered and the bow tie looks like a pair of butterflies in a dramatic mid-air collision.

I salute him.

"Good evening, Major."

O'Connor is still smarting from his treatment at the hands of the Met.

"Don't give me any of that imperialist crap. Come over here."

He ushers me into a corner by the Piccadilly entrance where my batman is enjoying a spot of below-stairs ribaldry with the woman who takes the ladies' coats.

"Listen, who is this woman whose fate you're trying inextricably to link with mine?"

"Rodney, I've told you before. Wendy. Publisher. Attractive. Friendly. Will laugh at your jokes. No inextricable linking involved."

"That's what you think. Women are always getting ideas about me. It's very demanding."

The only idea any woman will get about Rodney in his current state of dress is 'can I take him back to the shop and get a new one?' But I don't say this because I don't want to hurt his feelings. I can't think why; he revels in hurting mine.

"Who's the other one?"

"Sally. You've met her."

"Ah, yes. The shrieking girl who shows her underwear to the lads."

Sally, who now sweeps in, is not exactly shrieking, although her raucous laughter is enough to frighten an advancing party of German businessmen, who scuttle back to their trenches. And, true, bits of underwear are peeping out of her abbreviated cocktail dress as it simultaneously slips from her shoulder and above her knee. Wendy looks less at home. She is in a pre-Raphaelite number that runs greatly to lace and velvet.

There are kisses all round, Rodney included; he has decided to behave for the moment, it seems.

*

Persuading Sally to come to Tristram's ball was always going to be difficult; so I didn't try. Instead, she rang me and demanded to be invited.

"But you'll hate it!" I said. "You detest Tristram."

"It's no use trying to put me off for some floozy. I'm determined to go."

"All right then. I would have asked you anyway. Do I interpret this as a formal reconciliation?"

"I don't know what you're talking about."

Fortunately, I was without a partner. Lorraine said she was busy that night.

*

We are seated in the bar area, strategically placed to accost waiters and rubberneck at the front door. Sally leans over and taps O'Connor on the knee.

"Tell me about your love life, Rodney," she says.

"Sally!" says a reproachful Wendy. But O'Connor, unlike the rest of humanity, is not ruffled by Sally's tactics.

"There's nothing to tell," he says. "I am a married man."

"How lovely for your wife," says Wendy gallantly. "Couldn't she come tonight?"

"What's going on, Rodney?" I demand.

"Well, the lady wife isn't here tonight, largely because she doesn't exist." Rodney sits back, as if this were enough to settle the matter. He looks surprised when Sally makes a motion for him to continue. A standard O'Connor gambit.

"Oh, I see. You're wondering why I call myself a married man. Well, what I mean is that I am *temperamentally* a married man. Matrimony has marked me for her own. All the signs are there. The sullen domesticity, the furtive sneakings-out to the pub, the long days and evenings spent in resentful silence. In the more orthodox marriages you might expect more sex, granted. But I understand from my favourite women's magazines that the celibate marriage is by no means a rarity these days."

"But who stops you going to the pub? Who makes you sullen?" asks Wendy, pulling her hair. Rodney regards her balefully.

"Conscience, that's who. She's a real bitch."

Sally flops back in her chair and puts her feet on my knees.

"Another advantage, I suppose, is that you don't have to put up with mothers-in-law either," she says. "No soppy girl buying you enormous birthday cards and calling you Roddikins. You may as well get all the pathetic clichés off your chest. Of course, another variation on the wifeless marriage is for you to simply shack up with your drinking mates so you can sit in front of the television in peace, burping and farting to your heart's content. I knew a man once who said he couldn't share a flat with a woman because they were always hanging their tights up in the bathroom. Tights in the bathroom, really. There isn't a man's bathroom worthy of accommodating my tights."

It is one of Rodney's peculiarities that he relishes being attacked. I, meanwhile, wonder uneasily if the evening is spoilt before it has begun.

Rodney grins at Sally.

"It isn't just the tights," he says. "They wash their knickers in your sink."

"Gosh, men have some odd fantasies. Have you ever washed your underwear in a man's sink, Wendy?"

"No, but I've known men who leave their hankies under your pillow," Wendy retorts with spirit.

"Disgusting. Do you know why Mr Bachelor Boy Roddikins comes up with these clever evasions, Wendy? It's because he's afraid. He's afraid someone will get to know him and laugh at all these funny, beery habits he protects so jealously. The Randy Sleuth here is the same, only he pretends he's a New Man who changes his socks every day and cooks the dinner once a month. They're both cowards, really, running away to their pubs for a good snigger about the girlies. They're such cowards."

"I think that's a bit harsh," says Wendy, doubtfully.

"It's a travesty," I put in, feeling something is required of me. Rodney says nothing, but watches Sally with what in a normal person might be mistaken for deep affection.

*

The conversation subdivides.

"So. What are you going to do about the *Eye* article?"

"Nothing. I don't want to be involved in your grubby little affairs."

"According to them you *are* one of my grubby little affairs."

"Well, I thought it was a rather charming little piece."

"According to them, you are my charming little piece."

*

". . . and there's the barmaid in *Tom Jones*. A very important character."

"How many pages?"

"What did you say?"

"How many pages do you need to do justice to the barmaid in literary history?"

"I hadn't considered the matter."

"Cover?"

"Cover?"

"What goes on the cover?"

"A barmaid, perhaps?"

"*Un Bar aux Folies-Bergère* by Manet. Obvious."

"You're very commanding when you get on to your subject, you know."

"You should get in a proposal soon."

"Are you telling Rodney to *propose*, Wendy?" says Sally, who has been only half listening to me. "I'm glad someone is taking a firm line with him."

*

A young man in a well-tailored suit detaches himself from a mixed party of English and Japanese businessmen which is going into the restaurant. He comes over to us and kisses Sally on the lips.

"This is a bit upmarket for a girl of your louche tastes, isn't it Sal?"

"You don't know how louche I can be. Mark is taking me to a ball which one of his seedy PR men is putting on. I expect it will be full of bimbos and criminals and Mark wants me there to raise the tone."

"Oh, you're the celebrated Mark? How is the over-active donger? Don't mess about with my Sal or I'll cut it off. Listen, Sal, got to go in to eat with the Nips. Give me a call on Monday."

"Don't tell me what to do, please."

*

"But you haven't told me whether you're serious about this book or not."

"I'm more or less serious about everything. Waiter! I'd like a spot of Guinness."

"I'll ask the barman, sir."

"You don't really want a Guinness."

"Of course not. I just wanted to confirm the waiter's thick-skulled ideas about ham-fisted, drunken Irishmen."

"But how does he know you're Irish?"

"I might have let drop some incautious word to the effect that a bomb planted in the foyer might not be a bad thing. To avenge the great wrong done here to the pride of the O'Connors."

"What happened to the pride of the O'Connors?"

"My great uncle was thrown out of here in 1926 for distributing Republican leaflets to the diners."

"Gosh. Was he a member of Sinn Fein?"

"Jesus, no. He just liked a joke."

*

"So you think I shouldn't have believed Tristram?"

"Mark, you're such an innocent. *Of course* you should never believe *anything* Tristram says, particularly not one of his grubby little sexual fantasies. He really is the worst little spiv in London, and it never ceases to amaze me how he gets people like you in his pocket. And by the way, I won't believe this ball is happening until we get there."

*

Back in the gents', I am making some running repairs to the costume. Rodney is past repairing, so contents himself with splashing water on his face and saying ORRRRUSSSSSSHH! The batman eyes him sombrely, as if he's just found out that O'Connor has a German grandmother.

As I try to convince the tie to behave, I catch Rodney looking hard at me in the mirror.

" 'Are you serious?' she asks. 'Are you serious?' "

I frown, puzzled, at him.

"Your friend. The publisher in the Mary Queen of Scots outfit. I was telling her my barmaid theory and the damn woman starts talking about advances on publication and whatever."

"You ought to be very pleased."

"Like hell. The joy of my grand theories is that they are part of the oral tradition. They're not meant to be written down."

O'Connor is flushed and it isn't just the drink.

"It sounds as if Wendy has your measure, Rodney. And you know what the hero in *The Honorary Consul* says: every man has to find his measure."

"That's just the kind of smart journalistic play on words I'd expect from you. Well, while we're on the modern classics, here's another apposite quotation for you. Your friend Wendy is 'another illustration of how women are congenitally defective in sportsmanship.' "

"Hemingway?"

"No. A chap called Richard Gordon. *Doctor in Clover*."

CHAPTER EIGHTEEN

Despite Sally's scepticism, Tristram's ball is alive and tolerably kicking when we arrive. As we enter, she puts her arm around my waist and leans her head lovingly on my shoulder. Wendy, demure but firm, slips her hand under Rodney's arm and his face is eloquent with outraged bachelorhood.

Once inside, our professional antennae start twitching. We soon learn that Tristram's Category A celebrity is Fergie, and if any Duchess can properly be called right up Tristram's street, it is this Duchess. It is a coup for the boy and Sally has to fight hard not to look impressed.

Elsewhere, there is a heavy sprinkling of pop stars, film people, sportsmen and TV presenters, all with necks extended like hungry young sparrows' in search of other celebrities.

I find it quite comforting that when it comes to rubbernecking, no one can outdo your celebrity. They love being seen and above all being photographed, with other famous people. You can put this down to the David Niven factor: the desire to accumulate enough anecdotes about one's famous contemporaries to make at least two volumes of racy auto-biography. You can put it down to competitiveness – a trial of strength to see who gets the most attention, otherwise known as the *Hollywood Salutes Some Decrepit Old Fart in Three Gushing Hours of Prime Time TV* factor. Or you can simply put it down to status: the desire to see their own fame reflected in another person. There are some honest stars who carry auto-graph books with them: the majority are content with effu-sive greetings and paparazzi poses with more or less complete strangers.

Sally's face lights up. She has picked out one of her favourite celebrities: Jeffrey Archer.

"Jeffrey, darling!" she says, planting a big kiss on his cheek. A frequent ploy of Sally's is to apply twice as much lip-stick as usual before going to a party. Then she greets every man she sees with a huge smacker such as the one from which Jeffrey is now reeling. Then they, like him, are left with an enormous lip-shaped mark on their faces. Jeffrey manages to wipe his away with a handkerchief, but not before several passers-by have noticed and giggled.

"How are you, Miss Bretforton?" he says, sounding, as usual, like a hearty off-duty vicar.

"Probably drunk, my darling. Tell me, Jeffrey, I hear Mrs Thatcher is keeping a cabinet seat warm for you. Which one is it to be?"

"First I've heard of it," says Archer gruffly, but allowing his eyes to twinkle for the benefit of the audience.

"Minister without portfolio, I think. Or was it foreign secretary? I can't remember."

"Sally, is it possible to have an off-the-record conversation with you – non-attributable and emphatically not for quotation?"

She nods furiously.

"Good. Right then. There is absolutely no truth in this or any other rumour you care to dream up." He smiles and turns to go.

"You're so firm and manly, Jeffrey," says Sally, undeterred. "I love it when you come over all stern and non-committal. It's so unlike you."

"You're very charming, Miss Bretforton," he says. "I would write you into a play, only no one would believe such a mischief-maker could exist."

"That's not very nice. I think I'm a fully rounded, three dimensional character."

"I suppose you expect me to say, 'not like one of my characters', do you?"

"Thank you, Jeffrey. Read the paper tomorrow."

"You are quite incorrigible, Miss Bretforton."

But she has gone, dragging me with her.

*

"Well, Mark," says Sally as we stand by the bar. "Now it's your turn."

"What do you mean?"

"Fergie, of course. Get a quote. Get arfter her, son," she says, falling into Glotter-ism. "Dog her every footstep. Copy, copy, copy."

"I am supposed to be here on pleasure alone."

"Pleasure? You silly sod. This is newspapers, you pathetic young whelp," says Sally/Glotter. "Come on," she says in her normal voice, giving me a push. "Let's see the Randy Young Sleuth at work."

There is no way out. Lancelot must have felt the same way whenever Guinevere asked him to nip out and slay a few black knights for her sake. And I expect Lancelot called Guinevere an unreasonable cow under his breath a few times as well.

I go up the stairs and survey the battlefield. It won't be easy. As the Duchess moves around she is at the centre of an amoeba of hangers-on. I have little experience of royal amoebas, but this one looks awfully hard to penetrate. Sally catches my eye and makes a frantic gesture of encouragement. This discourages me all the more.

But once down in the main body of the hall, I spot a weakness on the royal flank. The amoeba opens up for a second and I dart in and am quickly one or two liggers away from the Duchess. Now it is just a question of hanging in there.

The party winds this way and that according to Fergie's whim and to the success of the dignitaries who try to ambush her. But with a good deal of apologetic wriggling, I work my way up to a strong position behind her left shoulder. She is wearing a kind of Elizabethan velvet number and might easily pass for Wendy's bouncy elder sister. I stay put while she talks to some wheedling nonentity. Then the amoeba is off again, wheeling its way around the dance floor.

By now, I am in a silent, dreamlike world, all movement dictated by the magnetic power of the royal party. I catch sight of Sally, Wendy and Rodney. Sally, her face red and tearful with laughter, calls out something which I do not hear. Wendy gazes pityingly at me as I defend my spot against an interloper. Rodney frowns in obvious perplexity.

As the party moves this way and that, I am gradually edged round in front of the Duchess. Soon, I may even be able to say something to her and get out of this hell.

Instead, Fergie decides to open the conversation herself.

"Who are you?" she says, crossly. "Why are you following me around?"

This is a very good question. Why am I following her around, particularly when I so desperately want to be Elsewhere? I must want something with this woman. What is it?

The dignitaries glare at me with the contempt of people who have been playing exactly the same game without being caught out. The Duchess looks hard into my face, waiting for an answer.

I say the first thing that comes into my head.

"I was wondering . . . er – why you're wearing an Elizabethan dress."

"Were you? Well, it's not Elizabethan. It was made by a modern designer. Now perhaps you'll leave me alone."

She turns away, but I am the one who is left alone. The rushing in my ears gradually subsides, normal aural service is resumed and I am conscious of a great sweatiness on my palms and the back of my neck. The people around peer curiously at me as I stand, stock still, wondering where my friends are.

*

I smoke a cigarette and walk moodily around the club. The celebs seem to have gone home early, thank God. There are just big, happy groups of people looking far more wholesome than you'd dare to expect of Tristram's invitees.

Sally has disappeared. This isn't fair; she is supposed to be here with me instead of laughing about my performance with Fergie to her friends. But I eventually find Rodney and Wendy.

As I greet them, and as Wendy asks me what's wrong, a tall man in a white DJ and red bow tie grabs her from behind, turns her around and kisses her full and strong on the lips.

Rodney makes a slight movement towards them as the kiss goes on well beyond the polite allotted time. Recovering her breath, Wendy introduces him as Garth. Garth is a property developer and a most unlikely pal for Wendy. I've met him before, although he doesn't seem to remember.

"Too many journos around here," he says, shaking my hand briefly. "Who's this fat bugger?"

"This is Rodney, Garth. He teaches at London University."

Garth bows.

"An intellectual. My favourite type of person. A man of letters. Let me kiss your hand."

"I'd rather you didn't."

"Fuck you, then," Garth says indifferently.

He puts his arm possessively around Wendy and his cheek close against hers.

"Don't know why you hang around with these wimps, Wendy. You could do much better. Take old Rodders here. Nice chap, I'm sure, but a bit podgy, isn't he? Not the kind of man to give a girl real satisfaction."

Wendy winces as he rubs her bottom.

"Garth, don't."

Garth lets Wendy go and turns to Rodney with a smile.

"Of course, Rodders thinks I'm some uneducated moron who's made a quick buck and thinks he can tell everyone what to do. Little does he know that he's talking to a product of the English public school system . . . and university. I've been to Uni, haven't I darling? That's where you and me met. I hated the place. Boring. Waste of fucking time."

"Perhaps you weren't ready for university," says Rodney.

"They weren't ready for me. Bores. Grumpy old gits. I tell you what, you meet some real bastards in the City, but nothing like those people. You're a bastard, aren't you, cocksucker?"

"Absolutely," says Rodney. "I count the day wasted when I haven't wrecked the character of some bumptious undergraduate."

"We hate academics, don't we, darling?" says Garth, squeezing Wendy to his chest.

"Some of my authors are academics. I don't hate them," says Wendy. "You're *hurting* . . ."

"We're going for a drink," says Rodney.

"See you later, Prof," says Garth. "Let me know if you want a hand fighting the women off."

Rodney is silent as we go to the bar. But it isn't one of his characteristic silences. This is not the silence of a man in control.

"What a jerk," I suggest. "Do you know, Wendy has the weirdest friends. There was this one bloke – "

"Sometimes I really fucking hate it," says Rodney suddenly.

"Hate what? Parties? Property developers? . . . Sex?"

"My job. I really hate my job."

"Well, I hate my job quite often."

Rodney stares at me for a second, then knocks back his whisky.

"You would."

*

I make attempts to start a dozen or so different conversations, but Rodney remains sullen. Finally, I leave the table, throwing back my chair with a fierce, frustrated gesture. Rodney looks unmoved.

Then, with bitter-tasting aggression mounting inside me, I find someone I like: Neil, my pop star friend.

"MY MAAAN!" he shouts, slapping my hands, ghetto-style. Then he bashfully thrusts his hands into his pockets, suburban housing estate-style and says, "How you doing?"

"Okay. My sources tell me you've made the Top Three. Congratulations."

"Thanks. Thought we were going to be stuck outside the ten, then we got *Wogan*. Always helps."

"But where are the leather-clad groupies and attendant drugs-pushers?"

Neil slaps his head.

"Shit! Must have left them in the car."

"And what kind of car is that? Some kind of giant phallus on wheels?"

"Well, no. It's a Renault 21, actually. Part of the record company package."

"The what? You sound like a computer salesman. I hope they give you a cocaine allowance, at least."

"I don't indulge. I don't want to sound like Bob Dylan."

The music from the disco thumps away behind us. Neil winces.

"Bit loud. And I'm supposed to be used to it."

"What else do you get with the package?"

"Oh, the deal's real def."

"Sorry?"

"Def."

"No, but the music is loud."

"You ought to be on the stage. Def. Definitive. Listen, I'm supposed to say all these things for the music press and you're not helping. The deal is rather good, if you prefer. Regular salary, expenses, the lot."

"*Expenses?* Jim Morrison, you should be living at this hour."

"We need some security. Okay, we're in the charts now, but we've got to think down the line. It's the album that really brings in the dosh. That's what we've got to get right."

"Is that why you're not drinking?"

"Too right. Recording tomorrow. I wouldn't have come, only the PR thought it might be worth a few column inches somewhere."

"I must say, Neil, I'm very worried about the decadent excesses of the modern pop star. Call me old-fashioned, but I think you should be wrecking hotel rooms and getting busted, not filling in your expenses claim and getting the Sierra serviced – "

"Renault 21. Not Sierra."

" – and living in Mitcham – "

"Not Mitcham. Palmer's Green."

"I despair."

"Listen, Mark, all that live fast die young have a good looking corpse stuff is boring, old hat. The kids want clean, friendly guys on *Top of the Pops*, not some washed-out druggy."

"And clean, friendly music."

"If you like. It's only beery old rock journalists who want you to act like a bunch of wild animals."

"But wild animals do have fun."

"So do I. And I intend to be still having fun in ten years from now."

*

More aimless wandering, more happy groups, no sign of Sally or Wendy. I may as well leave. Then I spot a familiar figure in the guise of an undernourished and slightly shabby Regency buck.

"Tristram! What are you doing out here by yourself?"

"Just chilling out."

"I was afraid you'd say something like that. Are you enjoying yourself? Is it going well?"

"Sure. It's going well, raising lots of money and all that."

"Then why so long in the face?"

"Oh, I don't know, I'm just bored. Everyone's having a good time, I know, but it's all a bit tame. No danger." He looks at his watch chain and sighs. "I was going to have a live sex show at this time, but the bloody management stopped me."

"Two boys talking about sex. I must join in."

"There you are. Tristram, have you met Sally Bretforton?"

"Surely," he says, kissing her hand. "Don't tell me. Opening night somewhere. You were with one of the Pet Shop Boys, weren't you?"

Sally doesn't know what the Pet Shop Boys are, but she catches the mood immediately.

"Oh, you mean that brilliant party where Rowan Atkinson did his stand-up routine? Brilliant."

"No, I know what you mean, but the one I'm thinking of is the one where Dudley Moore turned up."

"Oh, I remember. Brilliant, wasn't it? And David Owen in the corner with Edwina Currie."

"Sure . . . I think that was the one. I think I saw you talking with Sarah Brightman."

"Oh, well, you would have done because we went to convent school together."

"*Really*? I bet you've got some interesting tales from the girls' showers."

"Oh, hundreds. We girls often used to give ourselves all over body massages after hockey."

"Sounds like a club I belong to. But don't tell Mark. Your reputation will be stuffed in no time."

"Oh, I won't. He's tried to stuff my reputation on several occasions."

"I know, I know. Listen, starlets, my presence is required elsewhere. Got to lig. See you around."

We watch him depart, waving his lace handkerchief at people he spots along the way.

"I do like your friend Tristram," says Sally.

"No you don't. You can't stand him."

"I beg your pardon," she says in her best *Grand Dame* manner. "I think he's a very charming young man. Very innocent and unspoiled."

I simply can't cope with Sally. I feel too tired to follow the constantly changing rules of her games. And I'm too tired to hide the way I feel from her. She gives me a sharp look and her face instantly becomes serious.

"Your friend Wendy is having a good time."

"Don't tell me. She's making love with three cabinet ministers and the cast of *Cats*."

"Don't be silly. Come with me."

As I follow her up the stairs, a horrible suspicion grows in

127

my mind. Not the property developer, surely. Don't say she's gone off with him, please, no. That would be too much of a slap in the face to bear tonight.

Sally leads me to a small and strangely quiet committee room. There are a few couples sitting out, having simmering arguments or discussing their friends. At one end of the room are two young and rather pretty men, no more than 18 or 19. One of them is being kissed lingeringly and with every sign of relish by Wendy. The other stands close by, watching, a smile on his lips. Wendy doesn't see us.

Sally turns away with an odd look on her face.

"Well!" she says. "All this excitement is rather too much for me. Do excuse me for a second."

*

There is this girl whose name might be Sophie or it might be Emma. She might be a production assistant or an account executive, she might be a friend of Sally or a friend of Wendy: I don't remember. But I was introduced to her earlier in the evening and now, after two unsatisfactory hours, just as I am about to leave the club with a heavy heart, I spot her standing alone by the dance floor. We start talking.

Unlike everyone else this evening, she seems impressed with me. But then, I am not being shy about telling her what a glamorous, well-paid and yet artistically rewarding job I do.

Sophie or Emma is tall, has more highlights than *Match of the Day* and a solemn expression, as if she is permanently anxious that someone is making a joke that she doesn't understand. But her eyes, under their protective guard of mascara, are quick and intelligent. She is dressed simply in black.

The disembodied feeling I had when pursuing Fergie begins to return. Mark is a little drunk by now and is saying witty things to this girl he doesn't know about the dancers seducing each other a few feet away from us. I point out the secret buttock caressing and ear nibbling, the panting expressions, the hungry eyes. Sophie or Emma laughs in all the right places and we are bonded together in our superiority. Then there is a short silence while Sophie or Emma gazes at the dance floor and I gaze at Sophie or Emma. Then charming Mark suggests a dance with a joking promise of a few nibblings and caresses of his own thrown in. She says yes on the condition that she goes to the loo first. This does not seem unreasonable.

She goes and I stand around with the cares of the world gradually retreating as the promise of sex advances. Then something begins to trouble me, something itchy and nagging. It is either my boxer shorts or my conscience. The trouble seems to be in the brain region, so that rules out the boxer shorts.

The sounds of the disco fade away and the sound of warring voices in my head begins.

The conscience gets in the first blow. Conscience is represented by a female barrister of formidable intellect and negligible patience.

"Members of the jury," she says, "inspect the defendant. Note the immaculate wing collar shirt. Note the bow tie carelessly undone and oh so artfully draped around his neck. Note the agreeable smile he bestows on any passing unattached woman. Note the attitude of worldly, self-mocking good humour.

"And now, members of the jury, perhaps we should ask this fine specimen of New Manhood what he thinks of sex, and what he thinks of the sexual approach he is contemplating at this very moment.

"Perhaps we might suggest the following to him. That sex is a form of blood sport. That women are objects of the chase. That with a few drinks inside him and a few pretty girls around him, he acts like any other randy yob out for what he can get on a Saturday night.

"Of course, he will be deeply shocked at the allegation. Deeply shocked. This, after all, is a man who has read Germaine Greer. This is a man who told his last sexist joke in 1977. This is a man who detests those boorish members of his own sex who make no attempt to disguise their animal lust. This, members of the jury, is the New Man in all his finery, in all his sympathy and enlightenment."

The jury inspects me with interest as I lean against a pillar, trying not to look worldly and good-humoured and trying not to look at girls' bottoms.

"Now, members of the jury, shall we look more closely at our New Man?

"During the course of the evening, we may have observed some peculiarities in his behaviour. How, when he is talking to a woman, his eyes keep flitting to her breasts. How, when a woman passes him, those eyes cannot keep away from her figure. Women are used to being unclothed in public by leering male eyes. Any woman who has walked past a building site knows exactly what I mean. But how many of us admit that our smart office colleagues with their elegant suits and nice manners are just as lascivious? That the agreeable chap we meet over a business lunch is racking his brains trying to work out if we are wearing suspenders or not? And yet we all know it happens. I myself am continually harassed by male barristers trying to imagine the tiny black lace briefs I wear under my gown in court . . ."

The judge intervenes.

"Excuse me, Ms Conscience, but I feel the defendant is interpolating his own fantasies into your speech."

"Thank you, M'lud. That is just the kind of grubby behaviour to which I refer. I hope the jury took note.

"You may think this matter worthy of comedy – albeit of a rather pathetic order – as we inspect this young stud utterly powerless to control his libido for all his skin-deep liberalism. But I contend that this is a far, far worse thing that he is doing now.

"A young woman is about to return from the ladies' toilets. At this moment, perhaps, she is examining herself anxiously in the mirror while other girls around her unclasp their bras and dab Chanel No. 5 on their nipples . . ."

"Pardon me, Ms Conscience, but the defendant is interpolating again. Can I assure you, sir, that I take a very dim view of these erotic interruptions, and may I remind you that you do not have jurisdiction over this court even if these proceedings are taking place inside your head. I shall not hesitate to charge you with contempt if this nuisance continues. Pray go on, Ms Conscience."

"Many thanks, M'lud. Wise words, and a credit to your unworthy sex, if I may say so.

"As I say, picture this nervous, inexperienced young woman. Imagine the doubts running through her mind. Has she made a good impression on this sophisticated, witty young man? Is her hair right? Is he just after a one night stand, or is he – as he seems – genuinely interested in her?

"Perhaps, members of the jury, she has already fallen in love. Perhaps she is already convinced that he is not just After

One Thing. Perhaps she feels that, finally, she has found the caring, attentive, loving partner for whom she has sought after so many bitter, bitter disappointments . . . M'lud?"

"Ms Conscience. You are laying it on a bit thick."

"I am sorry, M'lud. I was simply endeavouring to give the jury an idea of the young lady's state of mind."

"Do so, by all means. But try to remember you are addressing a court of law, not writing a romantic novella."

"I will try, M'lud. In any case, I was about to conclude my remarks.

"Members of the jury, yours is an onerous task. Before you is a young, vulnerable woman and a man whose grotesque hypocrisy in sexual matters is, I hope by now, clear to you all. Will you send this girl into his clutches? Will you allow her to be seduced, then, in the course of time, and doubtless in his kindest, most decent, liberal way, be thrown on to the scrap heap? Think carefully."

Unaware that she is the focus of one of the century's most famous imaginary court cases, Sophie or Emma is taking an eternity in the loo. This is just as well, because it allows my counsel to stand up and have his say.

Counsel is an elegantly attired young man with a firm, if rather supercilious manner.

"Ladies and Gentlemen of the jury," he begins, "you have heard my learned friend present an articulate and interesting case against my client. You have heard him branded a hypocrite, a plausible rogue and a pitiless seducer. The Prosecution has argued with a passion that went far beyond the merely professional that to let this young woman – or 'innocent young girl' as she puts it – even enjoy a harmless dance with my client would be tantamount to an act of procurement. These are the charges.

"Let us first examine the motives of the principals involved. Broadly speaking, both are attending this party with one and only one end in mind: Fun. As a diligent columnist, Mr J is keeping his eye open for possible stories. But Fun, I contend, is the main reason for his presence here.

"And what about Sophie or Emma? Is not Fun, too, her guiding star?

"My colleague will have you believe that she is an innocent, waif-like creature, powerless against the demands of a male chauvinist society. With respect, this is the most ludicrous poppycock. We have all been here tonight. Have we not seen her laughing? Enjoying herself? And was I mistaken, or did I not distinctly see her pinch a male acquaintance's bottom? Let us not fall into error on this important issue: this girl is Having Fun, and intends to go on Having Fun. To suggest that she is some kind of miserable captive of the male ego is, I am sorry to say, an example of my colleague's outdated and blinkered view of modern womanhood. This girl, in short, can look after herself, thank you very much.

"And might I also ask the jury – particularly those among you who are unmarried – what is Fun? How would you go about Having Fun at a party such as this? Dancing, possibly, drinking, certainly. But most important of all, I suggest, you would look to enjoy the company of the opposite sex. I say this to male and female jurors alike. And let us be frank with each other: enjoying the company of the other sex often entails an element of seduction. Despite my learned friend's portrait of her as an injured innocent, Sophie or Emma is not ignorant of the rules of seduction. Judging by the form she has shown tonight, I would hazard that she has not always been more seduced against than seducing, by any means.

This is a game played between willing participants. My client is not playing Don Juan to Sophie or Emma's Elvira, Real Madrid to her Yeovil Town. This is not a gross mismatch.

"The Prosecution refers to my client's record as if he were an infamous safebreaker or con artist. I contend that there is *nothing at all* blameworthy in his amorous past: nothing that has not been motivated, not by lasciviousness, but by Fun and Chivalry – "

"Objection, M'lud. The Counsel for the Defence is speaking pure bunkum and he knows it."

"Perhaps we should allow Counsel to explain exactly what he means by the term 'Chivalry'. "

"Thank you, M'lud. It is a well established fact that, despite the social changes of the past two decades or so – changes of which my client heartily approves, incidentally – it remains the prerogative – nay, the duty – of the chap to 'make the running'. He it is who is expected to make the first amatory move: and I contend that not to make such a sign is a gross offence against chivalry. I don't say that making that sign is an entirely disinterested gesture. But it is nevertheless a selfless and generous act designed to make the little lady feel that the hours of preparation, the self-doubt, the agonising have not been in vain. It is then up to her how she responds to that gesture. It is a chivalrous, time-honoured way of proceeding; and one firmly in the traditions of Having Fun.

"And so, members of the jury, I direct your attention to Sophie, Emma or whatever her name is as she emerges, radiant with expectation, from the ladies' powder room. My client may or may not prove to be her Knight in Shining Armour. But I sincerely ask of you: will she not Have Fun finding out?"

He sits down and the judge hurriedly sums up.

"Members of the jury, you have about fifteen seconds to produce your verdict, so make it snappy. Should the defendant go for it or not?"

The foreman of the jury stands up.

"Go for it with a vengeance, M'lud."

CHAPTER NINETEEN

"Hello. Is the nose well powdered?"

"Beautifully powdered. Sorry I was so long. You have to queue for the mirror in this place."

"No worries. I was just having a debate with someone."

"A debate? How funny. What about?"

"Nothing much. I like this one. Shall we hit the floor?"

"All right."

On the sound system, Terence Trent d'Arby is getting very excited about something against a sultry backbeat, and the couples around us on the dance floor are in an advanced state of condensation. They lean on each other, breathe on each other, fondle, paw, hug and tickle, more or less in time with the music.

I put my arms around Sophie or Emma and she smiles at me. By the first chorus, our knees are touching. Knees aren't usually considered an erogenous zone, but in this mood, any-thing is likely to become erogenous – including the toes of my Church's full English brogue, which Sophie or Emma has just stood upon. My hand moves with the confidence of an orthopaedic surgeon to her lower vertebrae and with my middle finger I apply a significant pressure. Press for action, as the bank ad says. Sophie or Emma allows her thighs an extra, sensual, slow swing in response. We dart glances at each other like circling boxers, but we are now in the kind of clinch which no boxing referee could possibly allow for long. Sophie or Emma's cheek is on my shoulder and her breasts are pressed hard into my chest. The rhythm goes insistently on. Terence sings "Slowly, we make love . . ." Then he sings something like "WHOO-OH-OOH-YEY-URGH-HEY", the beat picks up and we make slow, stirring movements that would embarrass the most broadminded onlooker. Not that we give a damn about onlookers, broadminded or not.

The music ends, I gasp, Sophie or Emma lets out a funny, embarrassed giggle, but we stay in our clinch, separable only by a crowbar or the new Kylie Minogue single.

Then the DJ puts on the new Kylie Minogue single.

The thrust of my foreign policy is now to find a quiet corner where I can continue my orthopaedic research and where Sophie or Emma can do some more interesting things with her thighs. After that, it is only a matter of time before I speak the most romantic word in the English language: "Er-coffee?"

I am leading her to a promisingly under-populated area when she pulls me back.

"Sorry, Mark. I've got to pop off again."

"What? Your nose looks beautiful. More powder will only ruin the effect."

She smiles weakly. Mind, it was a weak joke.

"See you in a minute."

I collapse into a chair, light a cigar, steal someone's drink and allow myself to look perplexed. It's a bit rich. You go through agonies with your conscience; even now conscience barrister is probably considering a last-minute appeal, and I don't think I have the energy to go through all that again. Then, just as Sophie or Emma has convinced you that consciences aren't all they're cracked up to be, she turns out to be a fraud who prefers the company of other women with bladders as fickle as hers.

I wonder what has happened to my friends.

Sally has been a pain in the bum; rude, even. With Lorraine practically invisible over the past few weeks, I thought there might even have been grounds for a reconciliation between the two of us tonight. I am spending much of my time remembering what a wonderful lover she was, as opposed to what an impossible partner she is.

I am still gobsmacked at Wendy's performance. No, not gobsmacked: upset. It's not fair that I should be; if she wants to seduce pretty teenage boys, that's her business. But it seems very undignified. But there it is. I'm too drunk to rationalise any further.

And Rodney. I am most stung about Rodney, but I think I can explain it. I think he's fallen for Wendy. There was something very un-Rodneylike in the way he reacted to that prattish property developer. I think he's in love.

This is an event that occurs so infrequently that it deserves to receive the kind of media coverage accorded to Halley's Comet or a test match victory for England. Rodney limits his seduction attempts to once every two or three years. He chooses the occasion with the utmost care; the situation must offer the maximum potential embarrassment and discomfort for all concerned before he will pounce. On the last occasion, he laid the Dean of Faculty's daughter on the lawn outside the house where he, the Dean, was holding a cocktail party for the University nobs – nobs who could have wrecked Rodney's academic career with a word. Before that, it was the wife of a fellow don. The affair might have developed into something akin to D. H. Lawrence's elopement with Frieda. Luckily, they both got bored and Rodney was not obliged to write the sequel to *Lady Chatterley's Lover*.

On reflection, bonking Wendy on the floor of her flat to the rhythmic sound of her automatic Rottweiler isn't quite in the same league.

Still no Sophie or Emma. What is she doing? It could be Women's Troubles, of course, but then why? – no. Best not continue that train of thought. A more likely explanation is that the powder she uses is the kind you sniff through a used fiver rather than applying with a powder puff.

Then a waiter appears at the table. He tells me he was asked to give me these; 'these' being a bottle of champagne and a folded leaf from a Filofax. I throw the contents of my glass to the floor, fill it up with champagne and read the note.

SEDUCTION SURVEY
SUBJECT: J, Mark
TIME: 1 am
Mr J recorded the following scores. Marks are out of 10.

INITIAL APPROACH:	4
CHAT-UP LINES:	1
DANCING TECHNIQUE:	8
ROVING HANDS:	8
CROTCH CONTACT:	6

POST-DANCE CHAT-UP: 1
OVERALL SCORE: 28 out of 60 (46.6%)

JUDGES' REMARKS:
We were not impressed by a certain world-weariness in Mr J's technique. He needs to show more enthusiasm for the job in hand. It is all very well to seduce the first tolerably attractive woman that comes along, but he might at least make a token show of interest in her. But a reasonable attempt from this seasoned campaigner, all the same.
signed,
SOPHIE ROGERS
SALLY BRETFORTON

They will be watching me. Don't react. Don't swear. Do what then? Pick up the note, dip it into the champagne and eat it. Right. Delicious.

A camera flash and a volley of female laughter go off nearby.

*

Once again, I am wandering alone around the club, only this time it is with the determined stride of a man with a mission. Finally, I find Tristram. From the way he is trying to balance glasses of champagne on the bosom of the Liz Taylor looka-like he was with the other night, I conclude that his earlier subdued mood has passed.

"Tristram. I need your expertise as never before."

"No probs. Who do you want to talk to? Linda Lusardi? She's here. Rick Astley?"

"No, I don't want to interview anyone. I need a pair of women's knickers."

"Has your elastic gone?"

"Something like that. But how can I get a pair?"

"Easy. I'll ask Carmelitta."

He leads me over to a balcony which is supporting a woozy, heavy-lidded and handsome Spanish woman. Her hair is pulled back like a Flamenco dancer's and her makeup combines the colours of the Rio Carnival with those of sunset over the Andes. Carmelitta doesn't say much, having apparently lost the power of speech in the course of the evening's entertainment.

"Carmelitta, this is Mark. He wants your knickers."

Carmelitta nods and leans heavily on Tristram's shoulder. We shield her, rugby-player style, while she wriggles about under her tight red dress. Finally, she emerges with a pair of red silk briefs in her hand, which Tristram presents to me with a flourish.

"There you are. Hope they don't cramp your style."

"You're a star, Trist, a credit to the public relations industry. Thank you Carmelitta. I hope your nether regions don't get chilly."

Carmelitta sits down on the floor and falls asleep.

*

I track down the waiter and ask him if he minds doing another spot of going-between. The commission is the same: a bottle of champagne and a note. He nods.

"Perhaps you wouldn't mind giving them these as well?" I put the knickers in his hand. He takes them blank-faced. What service.

I go for another wander and another drink. When I return, my note is back on the table where I was sitting. Underneath, there is a message in Sally's handwriting:

"Even a five out of ten man can be a pretty quick worker. We'll keep the knickers in case you feel like tying them to your car aerial tomorrow."

*

I want and expect to confront Sally before she goes. We have a lot to talk about. Who emerged as the victor tonight? Why were we fighting at all? Why did she keep deserting me?

I still haven't tracked her down by the time I find myself standing next to Tristram in the gents'. I am there for the orthodox reason; he is busy with some polythene bags full of powder.

"Tristram, thanks for doing what you did. But I did ask for a pair of *women's* knickers."

"Well, they were."

"Perhaps. But it wasn't a woman wearing them."

"Carmelitta," he says, taking an almighty sniff, "may not be a woman yet, but she's working on it."

I wash my hands and get a shock when I notice the lank-haired, blotchy being into which J has degenerated during the evening. Tristram replaces his bag, gives a final sniff and peers red-eyed into the mirror.

"By the way," he says, "were you looking for that bimbo you came in with? Sally?"

"I was, actually."

"I've just seen her go. She left with that other friend of yours, the tubby one with the aged dinner jacket. Do they live together or something?"

CHAPTER TWENTY

The energetic columnist Mark J continues to look for female research assistants to help him with his many non-journalistic assignments.

His increasingly desperate search took him to the recent charity ball organised by foul PR man Tristram "the Spiv" Simms. Having made a pathetic attempt to get an interview with the Princess Fergiana, he sought consolation in the arms of on-off partner, gossip hack Sally Bretforton. Then he tried ex-floozy Wendy Dobbin of Sanctuary Publishing. Finally he turned to leggy art gallery assistant Sophie Rogers.

Fortunately, none of these sensible young women proffered the required secretarial help and the Randy Sleuth slunk off into the night swearing he'd "have the lot of them".

J's extravagant research programme is a costly business and the man described (by himself) as the Future of British Journalism is increasingly having to scrape the PR barrel. His latest important assignment is writing unctuous copy for a shady sales promotion company in the Home Counties. The message from the Great Hope is clear: anything considered.

CHAPTER TWENTY-ONE

The man on the phone wants to know about the ad.
What ad? My ad. Whose ad? Mine. The one with
my phone number at the end. But there isn't an ad
with my phone number at the end.

Yes there sodding well is. He's looking at it. But
my flat isn't up for sale. Who said anything about a flat? Then
which ad is he talking about? The ad in the phone box, you
stupid pimp.

Oh shit.

"I didn't put an ad in the phone box. Not me."

"Then why's your number at the end, then, mate?"

He reads out the number. It is mine.

"Where's Cathy then?" The voice is hard North London
and it is not that of a joking friend. It has the sullen, contemptuous tone of the bloke who says he can't mend your
central heating for a month or the bastard who fraudulently
adds £200 to the bill for your car service.

"I'm sorry. There is no Cathy here. You've been misled."
(Why should I say sorry to the filthy sex-starved git?)

"Don't be sorry, mate. Just get me a screw."

He hangs up.

I stare glumly at the phone. Last week, I played the Ansaphone messages and a foreign adolescent voice announced that he was gay and invited me to ring a number in the Bayswater area. The voice was stoned, high-pitched, nauseating.

So twice within the space of a few days I have been allowed these unsought-for glimpses of London's sexual underworld, and I am suddenly frightened. I want some homely, starched middle-class woman to come and disinfect the phone.

I go to the bookshelf and pick up the latest A.N. Wilson blockbuster to cheer myself up. But I cannot concentrate: the voices of the two callers, their stale, sweaty voices stay in my head. I seem to see the two sets of eyes: the man's lazy and malevolent, the boy's vacant, filmy.

*

It has been a rotten week. After the ball, I was angry. That was replaced by a mood of sadness and self-reproach. Now a feeling of utter disorientation has taken over.

The finances are looking disorientated too. Very soon, I shall be forced to make an interim financial statement to the bank manager:

"The directors of Mark J plc today warned of a drastic fall in profits for the first half. They blamed the shortfall on deferred payments from newspapers, which form the major part of J plc income, and on higher than expected costs, particularly in the alcohol and wardrobe departments. The directors added that future profits may also be adversely affected by the unexpected cancellation of several journalistic pro-jects. They insisted, however, that a wide-ranging cost-cutting programme was under way. In particular, they ex-pect expenditure in the restaurant bill area to be drastically reduced due to the sudden shortage of friends to dine with."

The first person I wanted to orientate towards was Lor-raine. She didn't return my calls. According to her secretary, she was successively on a shoot, in a meeting, out with a client and in another meeting. After being put off for the fourth time, I decided that I couldn't take the humiliation any longer. I don't know what game Lorraine is playing with me anymore; a month ago, we were becoming quite close again.

I don't feel like talking to Sally or Wendy and they ob-viously haven't felt like ringing me. Normally I would put the case in Rodney's hands. But in my current mood, I don't feel like playing Dr Watson to his Sherlock Holmes.

So here I am suffering from a bout of self-pity and in-decisiveness. I am beginning to feel like one of those poor lads from the North who sleep under the Embankment and are always being featured in the hard-hitting award-winning documentaries:

". . . this is the story of one of them, whom we shall refer to only as 'Mark' . . . Lured to the big City by the bright lights, the glamour, the promise of vast financial rewards, we find him alone and friendless in his increasingly decrepit North London flat (£70,000 still left on the mortgage), begging any commissioning editors that pass for the odd article just so he can get his daily fix of Chardonnay . . . deserted by friends and loved ones, this young man, old before his time, this sad symbol of the failure of 1980s Britain to provide a decent standard of living for aspiring young media stars, is increasingly forced to hang around the streets of Soho at night looking for any cheap thrills that might be going . . ."

The money may be running out, but at least the store of dramatising self-pity is full to overflowing.

*

In spite of the promise contained in my interim statement, I invite Ursula out to lunch. I want a shoulder to cry on, and although Ursula's is not my first choice, it is as amply padded as any in London. I have to talk to someone. We Type B personalities may like bottling up our emotions, but I don't want an ulcer to go with my broken heart.

We peer at each other over the small mountain of crustaceans that makes up the brasserie's seafood special. Ursula picks up a crab and sets about it with an implement I'd last seen in the hands of a dentist. My teeth ache in sympathy with the crab.

"She's just playing hard to get," says Ursula when I tell her about Lorraine's elusiveness.

"That's a very generous way of describing psychological torture."

She laughs as she continues to scoop out the crab's mortal remains.

"Come on, Mark. You exaggerate everything: psychological torture indeed. She's just acting like a teenage girl. She won't let you go, don't worry." She pats my knee, leaving a crabby stain on the knee of the new Paul Smith suit I have bought to relieve my depression.

I look dubiously at a prawn and dubiously at Ursula, who looks uncommonly like a prawn with her big ray-ban sunglasses and long nose. She gathers, correctly, that I want to hear more. She continues to gut the crab, her tongue peeping between her teeth as she concentrates.

"I know I sound flippant, Mark, but I'm serious. I find it very strange that you're pursuing Lori."

"Why?"

"Because she's a tart."

Ursula peers inside the shell of the crab. Her eyes, slightly watery now, still refusing to meet mine. She looks thin and angular, her bony shoulders barely covered by her silk summer top.

"I know it's only men who are supposed to say things like that. But if someone tells you that women don't sleep their way to the top anymore, don't believe them. She's had several flings with guys at her agency. I know of two for certain. She's a slag, Mark. I hate to say it, but there it is."

Two pictures of Lorraine are in my mind as Ursula talks. The first is of a long-haired girl in ragged jeans sitting in a pub smoking a hand-rolled cigarette. There is a deeply contemptuous look on her face and she is going on about boneheads and men in suits and how much she hates them. She used to go on about that a great deal. Too much. The second picture is of sun-tanned Lori in her short linen skirt laughing in a hotel bar in Cannes, being teased by a group of young admen in Hawaiian shirts, joking about the men in suits back in London. Ursula is right. I know it.

I look at the sickly pile of crab meat on my plate and the dismembered remains of the seafood. Everything in the restaurant seems flimsy, day-glo, throwaway.

"One thing I've never believed, Ursula, is that women who have careers are always bitching about each other. Now I'm not so sure."

Ursula's eyes are now very moist. Her fingers toy with an oily mussel. Still she doesn't look at me.

"I thought you'd be upset, Mark."

"Then why tell me?"

"Because someone had to." She speaks in a chilling near-whisper and there is fury in her face. "I know you hate me, but I am *not* a bitch, so . . . so screw you, Mark. You've got this ridiculous passion for this girl, this, this real *lightweight*. I just don't understand it."

"Let me help you. I'll tell you something no one else knows. Lorraine and I have known each other since we were teenagers. We were in love then. Since she's been down in London, something has happened to her. She's been seduced by this bloody, empty rubberneck thing . . . I don't know what it is. Sometimes I feel like the only person left who hasn't gone over to them. I want to snap my fingers in people's faces all the time and say 'Come on! Look at your-selves! Wake up!' "

In my anger I snap my fingers in Ursula's face. She catches them in her hands, holds them, and kisses them.

She lets go, leans back and acts out a long, delighted laugh.

"Oh Mark, you're so funny. Where do you get these things from? And Lori – or what did you say, Lorraine? *So* sweet – she's the Girl from Back Home. It's too sweet for words."

"You're making me feel very nauseous, Ursula."

She thinks of flying at me, but decides to keep on with the amused sophisticate act.

"Darling, it's very charming, and I'm sorry if I sounded cynical. I honestly didn't mean to. But darling, people grow out of old relationships, they grow out of old friendships. You can't carry people around with you like luggage all the time, or you'll never grow up. I'm sorry, but it's a fact of life. Don't you think you're being just a bit sentimental?"

I take a prawn's tail and fiddle with it, not looking at her.

"Yes, I'm being very sentimental. But then people don't change because their surroundings change. Lorraine and me might look like rubbernecked Londoners now, but it's only the skin that's changed colour. *'La forme d'une ville change plus vite, hélas! que le coeur d'un mortel.'* That's from a book: remember those?"

The fixed, amused look stays on Ursula's face as she gazes at me. Then, abruptly, the smile vanishes, she leans forward and picks up her bag.

"Well, Mark, are you going to storm out and make the big gesture or am I?"

*

There are more and more phone calls for Cathy. Twelve today, seven yesterday. Somewhere, a prostitute with terrible handwriting is sitting in her flat fidgeting with her whip and wondering where all her gentlemen friends are. Either that, or I have made a terrible enemy somewhere and that enemy is having a very good laugh.

*

My depression is deepened by boredom. The newspaper cheques hardly keep up with one credit card bill, let alone three credit card bills and a mortgage. So I have agreed to write a brochure for a sales promotion company. This entails two weeks spent at the desk writing puffy corporate non-

151

sequiturs and thinking of England – when I am not thinking of the fat cheque they have promised me.

I am pottering about my flat devising better things to do than brochures for sales promotion companies. These include the washing up; watching an afternoon film on the TV; paying a bill or two; ignoring several more; watching more TV; and staring out of the window renewing my acquaintance with the local pigeons.

I am engaged in this important task when the phone goes. Another of Cathy's clowns, no doubt. But no, it is Mike from the PR company, the four-letter man who asked me to write the brochure. He is also a mind reader, because he has evidently felt the waves of my apathy and resentment and decided to give me a call from his car.

The obligatory introduction over ("just going along the Cromwell Road – Christ, this traffic – which way to South Ken? Oh yeah, yeah, got it") he gets the telecommunicative meeting going in earnest.

"You know me, Mark. No bullshit. You know I've broken my back over this brochure. It's a big win for us and I want it to be right and I'm going to a meeting with them now to hammer out the strategic direction of the publicity thrust. Now, this is the thing. You're a great writer, mate, I love your stuff and I really wanted you to do this job for me, you know, because I really thought you'd latch on to the philosophy angle really quickly. But what I've got to tell you – and I'm sorry, but I've got to action this before the meeting – is that the stuff you've given me so far isn't right. This'll never do, to be frank, Mark."

"Famous phrase, 'this will never do,' " I say, trying not to yawn. "Jeffreys's review of Wordsworth, wasn't it?"

"Damn these messenger bikes. They should take the

bloody things off the road. Listen, Mark, the bottom line is that you'll have to rewrite. It's too negative. The directors of this company are breaking their balls to please their clients and you make them sound like a bunch of airy-fairy gentlemen who're above all this trade lark. It's too negative. Too subtle."

"Too much irony?"

"Too much of that. Save it for your journalism, mate."

"Too truthful?"

"Come on, Mark, be fair. You're a hack. You haven't always been the most truthful little boy in the world, have you now?" He sighs with frustration at my ignorance. "Look at it this way. This stuff you've given us isn't *sexy* enough. I don't know, it's like screwing with your knickers on."

You sleaze, I say to myself. But money, in the person of Mike, keeps on talking.

"Mark, I've written down some ideas. They're only words, but they'll give you a guide. Just try to get up to speed with what the guys are doing, okay? Where am I? Right. Here we go. Forceful. Dynamic. Thrusting forward into new areas. Unparallelled record of client service. Highly creative. Energetic. Adaptable. Competitive. Love a challenge. Service tailored to special client needs. That's very important, that last one, and there's nothing in your copy about it. Okay? Savvy? There're a couple more, but that should do for starters. A few pointers."

"There's only one problem."

"What?"

"The truth. The company, as you well know, is a bunch of middle-aged airheads whose business is based on sycophancy, sharp practice and copious helpings of gin and tonic."

"There you are!" says Mike triumphantly. "Negative!

Cynical. All the time. Jeez. Mark, I thought you were good. I thought you knew what you were doing. Do me a favour, all right? Just remember who's paying the bills. The client, right? The client. Do as the client says and smile as if you're enjoying every minute of it and let him believe that you think he's the most wonderful, brilliant guy in the world and his farts smell of roses. Fuck me, Mark. Do you think I don't have to grit my teeth sometimes?"

*

Cathy is a very popular girl. The calls keep on coming, most of them abusive. At this rate, I'll have to change my sex and start wearing PVC mini-skirts just to save the bother of explaining to these stags that I cannot give them the required satisfaction.

Finally, I call the British Telecom cavalry. After trying 15 different numbers, I eventually speak to someone who knows what the hell I'm talking about, unlike those of her colleagues who somehow went away with the impression that it is I who am making the dirty phone calls.

She suggests I either call the police or get BT to screen all incoming calls. Great. This means that anyone who rings will have to spend a trying ten minutes trying to convince some Kevin from BT that their intentions are pure.

On second thoughts, this might not be such a bad thing. At least they should stop Mike from getting through.

CHAPTER TWENTY-TWO

Mr Mark J is to attend a summit meeting with Ms Sally Bretforton and Mr Rodney O'Connor later this week. The announcement took the diplomatic world by surprise, given the severing of contacts that occurred recently between the J and Bretforton-O'Connor administrations.

In general, experts believe that both Ms Bretforton and Mr O'Connor have been pursuing a policy of isolating J since the Dover Street Charity Ball a fortnight ago. On that occasion, his sexual foreign policy came under sustained attack from Ms Bretforton, while the relations between J and O'Connor – formerly strong allies – have fallen into a state of mutual suspicion reminiscent of the Cold War at its peak.

For his part, J is pressing the Bretforton-O'Connor axis to confirm or deny that a secret alliance was concluded between them on that night. Rumours that such a deal was struck have been gathering momentum since the two superpowers left the ball together in the early hours.

Our Diplomatic Correspondent reports: Two very different explanations are being put forward for this unexpected meeting, called, so I understand, at the behest of the Bretforton-O'Connor representatives.

The first is that the new alliance will be presented as a *fait accompli* to Mr J and he will be invited to accept the new political reality that implies – or stuff it up his jumper. The second theory is that it will simply be three old buddies going out on the razzle together.

Time will tell. But considering the notorious unpredictability of the three powers – especially in the case of Ms Bretforton – no one dares at present to guess what the outcome will be.

CHAPTER TWENTY-THREE

Outside the Groucho, four or five breathless teenage girls are standing around. One of them darts to the window, peers in, then ducks down while the others shriek uncontrollably and dig her in the ribs. They are not looking for Rodney, so there must be a pop star inside. I give them an indulgent, elder-brotherly smile as I go in. They look suddenly serious and one of them says something under her breath which brings on another gale of giggles as I cross the threshold.

The bumping-into begins in reception, where I meet an acquaintance who is in film production, something the most casual observer would be able to tell because of the greyness of his hair and the loud youthfulness of his clothes. In an affectedly offhand tone, he tells me that the Princess of Wales was in the club at lunchtime with Wayne Sleep.

"Oh?" I say, turning up the affected boredom another

notch or two. "How nice for them. I hope they tried the asparagus." As he leaves, I make a hurried note to ring one of the Fleet Street diaries. Perhaps I can say that Di 'n' Wayne knocked off a quick *pas de deux* between courses, finishing off with the death scene from *Swan Lake* with their coffee. The diaries will want to know stuff such as what they ate and the things they talked about. Being too lazy to bribe the waiters, I shall just have to make it up.

It is a good, bustling, ogling night. The pop star is George Michael and he sits in one corner looking as much like an Eastern potentate as he can for someone who looks as if he should be running a kebab restaurant. Necks are also being craned surreptitiously towards Rowan Atkinson, whose craning abilities are a match for any rubberneck.

Rodney and Sally are sitting together on the same sofa from which Grizz put the solar system to rights. Rodney is slowly sinking into the cushions, hands deep inside his trouser pockets, deep in some far-fetched anecdote. Equally far-fetched is the new tweed jacket he is wearing. Its dominant theme is a searing, burnt orange vertical stripe which alternates with horizontal stripes of turquoise *à la Kevin*. Even more breathtaking is his new haircut. The few grizzled curls are still there, but only on the top of the O'Connor crown. All that remains of the sides and back are a few stubbly bits of auburn. He looks ten years younger, and none the better for that.

Sally has taken her shoes off and has her knees drawn up underneath her in the manner of the Little Mermaid in Copenhagen harbour, while her black skirt makes brave but doomed efforts to conceal her thighs. Her arm rests on the cushion behind Rodney's head and she gazes intently and fondly at him as he blathers away.

Rodney glances up briefly as I sit down and goes on talking. Sally twiddles a couple of fingers, but keeps her eyes fixed on him.

Rodney finishes his story, Sally laughs loudly and ruffles his hair. Rodney sips his beer and, finally, looks towards me.

"The demon lover in person. Make yourself at home."

As it is my club and Rodney is nominally my guest, this is rather a cheek. But I thank him nonetheless and sit down on a low stool a few inches from Sally's knees.

There is a slight disturbance behind me as a couple of George Michael-ettes are ejected. Rodney peers over my shoulder to see what is happening while Sally concentrates on the sleeve of his jacket, picking at the tweed. Teenage voices are raised in protest in the lobby.

"Probably a paid assassin from Andrew Ridgeley," I say.

Rodney and Sally don't say anything.

"Princess Diana was here today, lunching with Wayne Sleep," I say, risking my exclusive story in order to get the conversation going. "Half-pint meets half-wit."

"She's not a half-wit," says Sally, absently. "She's really very bright and very charming."

"You may be right."

I am banking on Rodney saying "and who might this diminutive Mr Sleep be?" or something. Instead, he says, "We know. Sally's already written the story for tomorrow."

More silence. This is unnerving. Sally is now staring across the room; there is a pinkness about her face which could either denote embarrassment or the over-enthusiastic application of blusher. Rodney's gaze, equally fixed and with something hard about it, is directed towards George's impromptu court. I am conscious of looking searchingly from one to the other, trying to work out why I seem to be as popular as Judas Iscariot at a reunion of the Last Supper boys.

"Has term ended yet, Rodney?" I say, trying simultaneously to sound hurt and aloof. "Just dossing until September, now?"

"No. I start work on Monday."

"Rodney is going to work on my paper as a features writer," says Sally.

This is outrageous.

"Of course," I say. "I'd forgotten. Someone told me about it."

"That's strange. Only three people know: Rodney, the editor and myself. It was only fixed up today. Perhaps the editor rang you up to tell you immediately?"

I have known Sally for three years. I have known her be bitchy, mischievous, scandalous and quite gloriously untruthful. Not until this moment have I heard her with so much malice in her voice.

I have got to fight this and, for once, say exactly what is on my mind.

"I think it's a fucking stupid idea." Rodney turns towards me with a look of mild contempt. Sally leans back, her arm still behind Rodney's shoulders, and gives me a strange, humourless smile.

"Rodney, you know what this is? Treachery. Bastard treachery . . . and hypocrisy. You hate newspapers. You always have. You've always set yourself above the kind of journalism we do, with some justice, and I respected you for it. Feature writing, God. Perhaps you'd better go over and talk to George Michael. I assume you know who George Michael is, don't you? You probably do. All the time you've been pretending to be the lofty, unworldly academic, you've probably

been writing on the sly for *Smash Hits* and *Harper's and Queen.*
Yes, *Harper's* will be right up your street. Sally can tell you
which aristocrats and actors you've got to crawl to. Perhaps
you can write an article on What the Well Dressed Don is
Wearing in this year's copping out season."

Rodney says nothing for about 30 seconds.

"I've always thought it a pity," he says finally, "that you
were so critical of your profession without having the guts to
quit it for anything else."

"What do you mean, 'a pity'? You sound like Sally."

Sally looks embarrassed. For me, rather than for herself.

Silence again. Our voices were raised and one or two people
sitting around are stealing curious glances over their
shoulders. I hope they get curvature of the spine. A man
facing me is looking straight at us and talking out of the side
of his mouth to the people beside him without taking his eyes
off us for a second.

One last try.

"Still, Rodney, I suppose you might be better at journalism than I thought. Reliable sources tell me that it was you
who sold those stories about me to *Private Eye.*"

"Don't be pathetic with your reliable sources, Mark," says
Sally. "Of course it wasn't Rodney."

"Someone on the *Eye* told me it was."

But the words sound weak and they know I'm making it
up. Why am I making it up? Habit? Or because I can't cope
with a truth such as the destruction of two very dear friendships which I am being forced to witness and which I can no
longer misreport to myself. I feel sick to the heart with the
mesh of fibs and counter fibs and half truths in which I am
caught.

"It's quite obvious who's been leaking those stories, anyway," Sally continues. "If only you'd stop to think."

"Who?"

A smile in which there is some of the old, teasing, lovable Sally crosses her face.

"Your friend Lori, of course."

"Oh come on. Why should she leak a story about herself being rogered on a boardroom table? Even you can't be that far-fetched, Sally."

She shrugs.

"I can see why you wouldn't want to believe it. She's not the kind of girl whose motives I can understand. But I do know she wants you off her back."

"And how do you know that?"

"Because a friend of mine who sleeps with her told me."

"And what is his name?"

"*Her* name, Mark. Her name. You're very slow. I thought you'd known this girl for years, and yet you didn't know she was a dyke. Funny, that."

My heart is beating and the weird, detached sensation I had at the ball returns. There is a fair amount of cigarette smoke around, but that does not explain the fug that seems to surround the bar and envelop my own brain. All clarity has disappeared and I am thinking slowly, slowly, turning thoughts laboriously and clumsily like pieces of a jigsaw puzzle, and the pieces will not fit together even though I keep trying them, clumsily and painfully, over and over again.

"Young man," says Rodney's voice. "A few minutes ago, you called me a traitor, do you remember?"

I mumble something.

"That's what you called me and if you think I'm going to let it go you're very stupid indeed. Because I am not the traitor: you are. You are the traitor, and the worst kind – the cowardly kind. The kind who isn't loyal to anything, the sort who won't stand up to anyone with strong opinions of their own. A yes-man of the first water. As long as I've known you, you have whined and moralised about the iniquitous profession you find yourself in, and how the people who employ you don't recognise the fine feelings of which you're so proud. Then off you slink and write more mediocre, throwaway stuff to bring in your £30,000 a year."

I feel suddenly, angrily bored with all this. Just finish the speeches and get the sentencing over with, God damn it. But Rodney is in full flow, and the torrent of words I used to enjoy listening to so much goes on and tediously on.

"And your sex life is treacherous, isn't it? A simpering, weak-willed sort of treachery, betraying people out of laziness. The appetite not of the great lover, but the pathetic chocolate addict, unable to resist the most trivial temptation. That's true, isn't it?"

I may as well leave. Earlier, I was feeling like the schoolkid whose friends suddenly turn against, the puzzled forlornness of the bullied. Now I just want to go and get on with my life somewhere else.

I look up and notice Sally. Astonishingly, there are tears in her eyes. Rodney sits, sneering and waiting for my answer.

"So who have I betrayed, Rodney?"

"Whom? I don't know how many. Sally for one."

"That's not true. We only went out for a short while, and she didn't want to go on any more. And we're still friends. Or we were until you started acting like the Inquisition."

Everyone in the club is listening, or seems to be. The waiter is waiting to put the drinks down on the table next to us.

Rodney heaves himself forward and grasps my wrist. Holding it in a handcuff grip, he talks in an urgent stage whisper:

"Giving someone the clap is a form of betrayal, isn't it?"

The waiter comes between us and puts the drinks down. I am doing corny things like sweating and turning pale. I turn to Sally, who is crying.

"It can't be true."

"It can be true and it is," she says with a catch in her voice. "NSU. It's not too serious. Can cause infertility in women, just a little tingling in the willy for the man. Haven't you got a tingling willy, Mark?"

"No. No I haven't, honestly, I don't know what all this means. Truthfully. I never knew – I don't know how it could have happened. I'm very careful." Rodney makes a furious sound and throws himself back in his chair.

"Don't bother explaining, Mark," says Sally.

"You'd better go," says Rodney, forcing himself to sound indifferent. "We're going out to dinner."

I get up and leave.

CHAPTER TWENTY-FOUR

In a stormy and often bad-tempered debate, opposition speakers today demanded an "exemplary punishment" for Mr Mark J following the allegation that he communicated a sexual disease to Miss Sally Bretforton.

They demanded a complete list of others potentially infected in the course of what one speaker called "his disgusting and licentious career". "There are no terms strong enough to describe this nauseating disclosure," he added.

A spokesman for Mr J said he profoundly regretted any pain or distress caused to Miss Bretforton, but refused to comment on reports that other women may have been infected until more precise medical details were known.

The spokesman went on to condemn the opposition attacks as "way over the top".

"Mr J has already suffered greatly at the hands of friends whom he previously had good reason to count among his closest and most trusted. Naturally, he is in a severely depressed state at present and simply wants to contemplate his future in peace."

CHAPTER TWENTY-FIVE

I swallowed the Ecstasy pill at about seven, took a cab to Soho and now I am in Kettner's washing the thing down with a glass of champagne.

I'm not a frequent user of Ecstasy or any other designer drugs. You try the new ones as it comes into fashion and as long as it doesn't hurt. You see how it feels; you see what the papers are getting upset about. I don't rush to repeat the experience. There are enough illusions in my world without encouraging more.

I have always been suspicious of the secret, conspiratorial group of media druggies who find enlightenment by lining the pockets of Colombians whose idea of free market economics is to bump off your competitors with a chain saw. And these enlightened media druggies, let's not forget, are the same caring media greens who will tear your throat out for using non-biodegradable washing powder because it affects the quality of their enlightened lives. In the past, I have always had too much respect for my faculties to have them speeded up, slowed down, expanded, distorted and artificially messed about. I like to do those things for myself.

All this was true until the past two weeks. Now, my faculties have gone down dramatically in my estimation. The pill is like an Alka Seltzer, only it isn't my digestive system that is on the blink, but my life. In almost every department there are ominous rumblings and gurglings. The career tract is refusing to pump money with its usual regularity and is in severe need of a tonic. The love life is acting like an overworked liver, producing conflicting signals and sharp, unbearable pangs that bear witness to years of over-indulgence. The mental reflexes are sluggish. The feet are leaden. There is a tendency on the part of the patient to look gloomily on everyone around him. All things considered, the J system has degenerated into a collection of outraged and upset organs.

The best I can hope for is a respite courtesy of the clumsily manufactured drug in my hand. I don't like the word Ecstasy: it offends my personal Trades Description Act. Slight Lessening of Agony might be more appropriate.

Before long, I am conscious of a slightly woozy sense of well-being. I start beaming vaguely at the dark, pleated boys and girls enjoying their Thursday night out. Someone is arguing with the barman because he refuses to serve beer in the champagne bar. Their performance of bad temper seems to my eyes charmingly acted and quaintly reminiscent of little children stamping their feet at some adult outrage.

I lean against the bar luxuriating in my role as Outcast, Observer Made Wise by Bitter Experience. Everyone in the bar seems to be putting on pretty theatrical sketches for my entertainment and to please my critical eye. In a corner, a buxom girl leans over and pinches the nose of a middle-aged man in a leather jacket. I pan round, and two thin boys are sitting on two large girls' laps. In a group by the door, two women are talking to other people with their backs to each other, and every now and then their shoulder blades or buttocks touch, but they make no sign of surprise or indignation. George Melly wanders by on his way to a party upstairs, looking more George Melly-ish than anyone would have thought possible. He has a hearing aid: a bizarre sight, a mechanical reminder that there is an OAP beneath the canary yellow and green checked suit. Next to me, a man in tinted glasses with an unpleasant moustache is comforting a crying, pretty 17-year-old girl who is perhaps drunk, sick or pregnant. She grips her tulip glass and avoids looking at him. A wise precaution. I nod encouragingly at her. She looks up, snivels, and turns her head away.

Rather cleverly, Ecstasy has made me into a detached, Augustan figure who may or may not go home and write an epic poem in heroic couplets about the evening. The people who come in here must wonder who is this enigmatic chap at the bar with the sparkling eyes and quiet smile. Surely they do not say to themselves that here is a man with a stagnant career, a dwindling number of friends, a screwed-up love life and an infected willy.

For I am not the me who sat hunched on a stool in the Groucho stumbling over his words, disgraced, defeated at every turn. That person is a small, perplexed character, worrying over silly, conventional matters. In my expansive good humour, I picture that person with his funny, furrowed brow, forever agonising over what others think of him, so different to the Olympian, Ecstatic me, on a perch where I survey others, indifferent to being surveyed myself. I snigger to myself when I think that my appearance was once a source of more or less permanent fretting. The lock of hair over my eyebrow is decorative rather than irritating. The loud pattern of my tie is a perfect foil to the subdued grey of my jacket. The trousers hang perfectly, the shoes are just right from any angle. And as I wander contentedly to the exit, past the arguing couple, the thin boys, the large girls, the buxom woman and the middle-aged man in the leather jacket, I am at home, at ease. There is a warm breath of wind outside in Romilly Street, the people in the street return my smile and as I stroll through Soho it is with the deep, happy sense of peace that a country gentleman feels when inspecting his estate.

*

There is a première of a new Ken Russell film in Shaftesbury Avenue; a newspaper gave me a ticket to report on the evening, or at least, they gave a ticket to the conventional, furrowed-brow chap who formerly inhabited my body. The new me might give the newspaper more than they bargained for in terms of reporting. So off I go on my merry way.

The audience are already milling outside the cinema, showing off to passers-by. They are split up in the following way: 20 per cent liggers, recognisable by the full drinks in their hands; 65 per cent friends of Ken's, recognisable by their taste for extravagant and fussy clothes; 15 per cent professional invitees, recognisable by their embarrassed expressions whenever one of Ken's friends sweeps majestically by in a cloud of dubious scent.

I am lounging outside the cinema still being the eighteenth-century hero of the couplet, wishing I had a morsel of snuff with which to punctuate my private *aperçus*.

A woman hands me a leaflet. She has her hair piled high, exotic sweeps of makeup around her eyes and a tassled skirt. She is also, I can't help noticing, completely topless. She appears to be something to do with the film, although in my present state I wouldn't be taken aback if someone told me she was modelling the new uniform for central London traffic wardens.

I plunge into the cinema in a shoal of the most bogus people imaginable. There are middle-aged women with loud, deep voices and unbecoming clothes. There are young men trying to look and sound like Oscar Wilde; sadly, their command of English has more in common with Larry Grayson. There are artistic lions from Chelsea whom no one beyond Chelsea has ever heard of, and their thin girlfriends whose duty it is to look panic-stricken whenever the artistic lion becomes drunk or offensive. There are flowered waistcoats, bare chests, purple wigs, mannerisms, gestures, little scenes and anecdotes extravagantly acted out.

The Ecstasy is working powerfully; it takes hold of me and gives me a jolt. When the jolt is over, I am overcome with the feeling that this is a dangerous place to be. Dangerous, because the people around me with their silly clothes and neurotic faces seem themselves to have an all too tenuous grip on reality. Where I need to be tonight is at a dinner held by some senior chartered accountants where everyone speaks sensibly about commuting and mortgage rates and the junior audit clerk who gets noticeably tipsy is the subject of much excited chatter. If you had an epileptic fit here, it would simply be interpreted as an impromptu display of performance art. But there is just enough Ecstatic buoyancy left inside to keep me from choking or screaming as I am propelled through the crowd.

171

In the foyer, the manager slides his hand down the three, carefully plastered locks on his bald head, down to a red neck bulging over the large collar of a tight dress shirt. He too is losing his grip, only, unlike myself, he is fighting every inch of the way. As a woman balances a bottle of champagne on her turquoise wig, he bounds into action with an agility born of self-righteousness. The manager lays two wrinkled hands on her bare shoulders and asks her to desist. She looks momentarily frightened and caught out; then she recovers and attempts to stick her tongue up his nose.

In the cinema, I stand surveying the scene with narcotic wariness. Like the rest of the rubbernecks, I am feeling uncomfortable. As good conformists, we agree with the critics, and the critics agree that you should not like Ken Russell films. Still, it's important to go to a Ken Russell première so that you can laugh at it afterwards and tell everyone what a bogus old charlatan he is. There will always be a serious type who says that he is not a b.o.c. but a powerful and innovative talent who is simply prone to excess. Then you can laugh at the serious type as well.

"You here to watch the movie or the tits?" says a New York voice behind me. It is Kae, a photographer's agent and an old adversary.

"It's hardly my fault if a promotional gimmick shoves its breasts in my face," I say severely. "Besides, I'm a bum man." I pinch Kae's through her jodhpurs. She, being American, pinches mine in return through my Chevignon chinos. Let's all clutch each other's designer togs, why not.

We sit down together. Kae is a good person to watch the film with because she is a token Bohemian (every good left-wing council insists that you employ at least one). She is of a 1920s vintage, as opposed to the rather poor 1890s apes around us. Kae is all Unconventionality, coloured tights, cropped hair and masculine gestures. She is short only of a cheroot and a monocle. There is one Christmas present problem solved. I am doing my best with a purple tie covered in art deco blobs but I can't really compete.

Kae takes off her shoes and unconventionally swings her leg over the arm of the chair, momentarily disconcerting the Oscar Wilde clone within smelling distance of the foot in the coloured tights. The bare breasts wobble by.

"You're leering again, sweetie," says Kae.

"And you're trying to be shocking. It won't work. Everyone here is trying to look shocking. You'll have to try harder."

"Don't be facetious, darling. You're too *nice*."

We watch the film and make tutting noises in all the right places. About half-way through, I get the fidgets, the nibbles, the numb lip and other Ecstatic side effects. Kae looks knowingly at me.

"Want to go to the bathroom?" she asks solicitously. "Looks like you had one too many pina coladas tonight."

*

After the film, we all congregate in the foyer and the acting outrageously competition begins in earnest. The manager is fighting off the woman with turquoise hair who is trying to dance with him.

In a corner, I spot a PR lady I know. She looks leggy and elegant, if somewhat fluttering, in a filmy long dress. I wander over to be charming.

Suddenly, 20 lights go CLICK! Only one group of people can make the lights go CLICK so loudly; sure enough, the

Paparazzi are trained on us. We stand there, the PR girl and me, with the mob snapping furiously at us. I don't know whether to feel like a film star or a disgraced politician and the logic of my imperfectly functioning brain tells me that I must be one or the other.

So this is what celebrity feels like: it hurts your eyes and you can't move more than a few feet for a group of sweaty men in leather jackets. For a few, frozen, framed seconds we stand like exposed people in a lightning storm. Between the flashes are occasional glimpses of shadowy, excited faces staring at us.

I look towards the PR girl expecting her to be as befuddled as I am. But the PR girl has changed. Her shyness is still there, but it is now a teasing, knowing shyness; she is a perfectly composed picture of nervous young womanhood, and looks as if she has been posing as such for the whole of her life. After one glimpse of her pale face, slightly parted lips and amused eyes, I realise the clicks and lights are not meant for me. I head for the background, quickly.

Kae is by my side.

"So what did you say to Brooke Shields, then, you sleaze-bag journo?"

"What?" I look at the woman I took for the PR girl, still exhibiting herself to three rows of photographers, grinning like Roman plebians hoping for *largesse*.

"I don't remember. Are you sure that's her?"

She looks suspiciously at me.

"Of course I am. You're supposed to be a what do you call it, a rubberneck, though where I come from that's what we call Brits who can't walk in a straight line because they're looking at the skyscrapers. Either that, or its some athlete who can manage auto-fellatio."

"It's all part of the same phenomenon."

I feel secretly triumphant that I didn't know who Ms Shields was; a private triumph to compare with not looking at your reflection in office windows or avoiding Langan's.

"Are you coming to the party?" I ask Kae.

"It may be my age," she says. "But I don't find 1970s weirdies as entertaining as I used to. You go by yourself, darling."

On to Ken's party at a place I am too Ecstatic to recognise. Inside, more wine, more bare breasts, and more unconvincing Bohemianism.

At some point in the evening, I have lost my eighteenth-century restraint and become a debauchee of the late Victorian poet type instead. I am now melancholy, drowsy as if of hemlock I had drunk. Moreover, my body is inflicted with a variety of aches, stingings and snufflings, not to say blurred vision, unsteady movements and an impulse to sing tunelessly to myself. I could easily pass for Swinburne after a heavy night out with the lads.

I sidle up to Ken Russell. Ken looks just like a Roman emperor, mainly because he is dressed as one. A laurel leaf sits on the kind of snowy white hair that properly belongs to a far gentler man. Ken is not a gentle man, however, and likes throwing people – particularly journalists – to the lions. Happily, he seems quite relaxed at present, dining on a cheese sandwich rather than the innards of some unfortunate critic.

Russell is talking with one of his hangers-on and Lorraine, who has her back to me.

I get closer. Lorraine's dense, long hair is imperfectly held in check by a silk ribbon. She wears a long t-shirt and faded jeans with some flowery Liberty patches on her bottom. Her long, beautiful neck and strangely long and firm jaw line are inclined to the left as she listens to director and hanger-on. Closer still, I see her straight back, her shoulder blades and vertebrae prominent through the thin cotton of her t-shirt. As Russell talks, her right hand slides up her neck and feels the ribbon, then falls gently to her side. The thumb of her left hand is hooked inside her back pocket.

Tonight, I have taken a tablet of a chemical which produces an intoxicating gas around your head for six hours, a multi-coloured, multi-odorous gas that makes you laugh, cry, eat, drink, pee and shout. Now the gas is evaporating and I draw the sharp, stabbing breath you take when you see the person you think you have fallen in love with when you are too young to know what to do next. It is morning break at school, I am 16 and Lorraine is dressed in a ghastly green uniform and woolly tights. I am again looking secretly at the beautiful neck and wishing with all the gushing urgency of an imagination just beginning to be fired by romantic poetry rather than Alastair MacLean that I could kiss the nape and stroke her hair. Lorraine is talking to her girlfriends. She doesn't laugh very much, even at this age, and the other girls look at her with respect and eyes that watch carefully for a sign of weakness that never comes.

Hot and blushing, I edge around so that she can see me from the corner of her eye. Russell keeps talking and the hanger-on frowns briefly at my intrusion. Lorraine makes no sign.

Ken is talking about baked beans.

"The last time I did a commercial was in the sixties for a baked beans company," he is saying. "The idea was to get a shot of a kid eating a spoonful of beans then beaming at the camera. Unfortunately, we had to spray the beans with some chemical or other to make them look appetising, and every time the kid ate a spoonful he threw up. Then some great hairy, sweaty member of the crew would rearrange the beans with his bare hands and the kid would throw up again. I think we got the shot on about the eighth take."

I laugh supportively. Lorraine remains with her head inclined towards Ken and away from me, but her eyes dart quickly in my direction.

"The whole business is morally putrid," says the hanger-on.

"It is morally putrid," says Lorraine, indifferently. "You know a lot about baked beans, don't you?" she says to Ken. "That scene in *Tommy*."

"Well, baked beans are better behaved than most actors . . ." Ken is beginning to say. Then the woman in the turquoise wig sweeps him away, with the hanger-on hanging on to their coat tails.

I am facing Lorraine now. She puts her hands in her pockets and looks seriously into my eyes. There is nothing left of her teenage sullenness. Now her expression is coolly searching as she absorbs me. Then someone brushes her back roughly as they pass and there is a sudden flicker of desperation in her eyes. She takes her hands out of her pockets and places them gently on my shoulders. Then, with a sudden, impulsive movement, she embraces me, fiercely, without a word, her forehead pressed hard into my shoulder, her fingers neurotically clawing my back. She looks up at me with red eyes and my own dim eyes can't make out if her eyes are red because of drugs or tears. A line of spittle runs unheeded down her jaw. For the first time, I realise that she looks unloved and unkempt.

"What are you doing here?"

"I came looking for you," she says and embraces me as fiercely as before.

"Why haven't you come looking for me before?"

"I love you," she says. "That's why I'm here. I've been looking for you because I love you. Love you, love you. I want to get married. Have children. Run away. Anything."

Her head is pressed painfully against my chest. No one in the room seems to care what we look like although we are welded together so clumsily.

I do not think that I believe her.

I want to grab someone and shake them until they tell me if she is telling the truth. But the milling people are all mad, their faces vacant except for the tinge of hunger, hunger for food, drugs, drink, sex, celebrity. They are grotesque figures exaggerated by the drugs in my head, or, worse, not exaggerated, real people acting the part of themselves.

The fug has again descended on me and this moment is not what it should be, is not the moment as I read it described in books. I blink to clear my vision, but all I can see is Lorraine's head upon my breast. And within my breast there is hate and desire and resentment and confusion. Lorraine grips the collar of my shirt so that it pulls painfully on my neck. I force her away from me. I will try to clear my head by shaming her.

"You're supposed to get on your knees if you're going to propose," I say.

She looks at me with irritation in her wet eyes:

"I am on my fucking knees."

"And you'll have to improve your language if you're going to mother my children. Why are you on your knees? Don't be self-pitying."

Lorraine steps back, takes her ribbon and twists it between her fingers.

178

"Oh, nothing much," she says, not looking at me. "I'm about to lose my job. My boss thinks I screwed one of the clients when I was supposed to be having an affair with him. Oh, and a man tried to rip the knickers off me in Greek Street last night. I'm pissed, doped up, fed up and sick, sick, sick. And I love you."

"You make that sound like the worst of your troubles."

She puts her arm around me gently and kisses my neck.

"What's wrong, Mark? What happened? You used to be so kind to me. Then I met you when I came back from LA and you weren't kind, you just wanted me. I don't know, London has ruined you or something. Why don't we go away and you might learn to do more than just want me?"

The truth is lying around somewhere if only I can find it. But I cannot seize on the truth in the words Lorraine speaks, words that are no longer the clipped-sounding, sincere ones she used to speak. Her voice is now lilting, mid-Atlantic mid-Chelsea. I am fighting hard to find something inside myself for her.

"I'm on my knees as well."

"Tell me," she says with a smile.

"My life is a mess and I've given Sally the clap."

Lorraine laughs delightedly and loud. It is a laugh which would stop a crowded restaurant in mid-forkful, but a laugh which no one notices in this unreal, screeching place. She makes a grab at my crotch. I fall backwards, crouching away from her.

"That thingie's all right, Mark. Sally's thingie's all right as well." She laughs again. "Let me tell you, I know all about this Sally. All about her. She's teasing you."

"How do you know?"

"Oh, it's all part of her campaign."

"Campaign?"

"Against you. Haven't you noticed? The *Eye* pieces. Spreading stories about you and me. Now putting it around that she's got VD from you. Even I think that's going a bit far, mind. Have you been for a test?"

"Not yet."

"Go on. You'll have yourself a nice surprise. A girlfriend of mine is very good friends with Sally. I don't know the whole truth, but apparently Sally wanted to like you once. Then, I don't know, she decided that you weren't good enough in all sorts of ways. I don't know the real truth at all, it's just a story I've heard. She's a bit of a snob, isn't she? And she's a very moral girl, isn't she, so she decided to give you a lesson."

"She never told me I wasn't good enough. I don't know what that means. I don't know if I believe your story."

Lorraine shrugs her shoulders and arches her eyebrows in indifference. Sally or Lorraine: which one do you believe? Which one do you love?

Lorraine knows what I'm thinking.

"I can't understand why people are always falling madly for Sally from what I've heard of her."

"Can you not?" I am trying to be formal, trying to look down at myself from above and judge my actions. But I am suffering from reality starvation and my head is light.

"Poor Mark," she says, noticing the anguish on my face. "People do take you for a ride. I almost feel sorry for leading you astray now."

"Which occasion are you referring to?"

She laughs again.

"Oh, you probably won't remember. We came down to London once and you and your mates were being boorish, so I pretended someone had made a pass at me in the toilets. It just seemed like a good idea at the time. I suppose I just wanted some attention. But don't look so sad. Are you coming home with me, or not?"

CHAPTER TWENTY-SIX

The alarm goes at 7.45 am. Once the heart-stopping shock of consciousness has passed, I slowly and resentfully begin reviewing the day ahead. Without even glancing at the diary I can guess the contents of the debit ledger: three potential writs, as many potential confrontations with editors and victims of past stories, boring brochure work, a dull lunch and a tiresome party. At 7.45 am, the credit ledger is empty.

Then I remember that it's Saturday. Feeling like a reprieved prisoner, I pick up the alarm clock, throw it with commendable aim into the waste-paper basket under the dresser on the other side of the room, grunt, hug the pillow and compose myself for rest.

"UP, UP and UP, lover," says a wide-awake voice on my left. Long fingernails tickle the back of my neck, walk playfully over my shoulder and settle in my chest hair.

"Furrrrrrrr . . . Saturday."

"Oh furrrrr nothing. It's nearly eight. UP, UP, UP."

The fingernails tickle my ribs but I am not going to give in. I turn round and grip her wrist.

"Come on, Caro," I plead, looking into her teasing blue eyes. "Give a worn out old sod a rest."

She smiles.

"You're very decadent, and you know your regime says that you have to get up early – Carlos is so strict, isn't he? I suppose that's why he's so good – but I'll let you off this once."

I lie back and close my eyes. Then I feel the nails again, this time pressing experimentally on my midriff.

"Mmmm . . . looks like the Carlos regime is having some effect, though. What's your read-out?"

"I don't know. I have conveniently forgotten. Carlos is a dictator and I hate him."

The mouth next to mine melts into a satisfied smile.

"Carlos says it's good to hate your coach because the adrenalin works better or something, and I can see what he means really. It's just the same in business."

The pressing restarts and the fingernails reappear admonishingly on my nose.

"Now, don't you feel better for not having drunk anything last night, lover?"

I open my eyes and stare at the ceiling.

"Having drunk nothing yesterday evening, I feel nauseous, bad-tempered and lethargic."

"Well, it's always like that when you're conquering an addiction, and when's the last time in the last ten years you can say you had a night off the pop? Your units must be well down on the week, though, so you've made a start."

Her face settles simperingly next to mine on the pillow and her lips pout to meet mine.

"You're a drunken old Bagpuss, but we're going to reform you and I love you," she says. We lie in each other's arms basking in the sheer niceness of the wonderful, lovely thing that is happening to us.

Thirty seconds of this and then Caro springs to her knees, playing havoc with the duvet, which I retrieve from the floor.

"And now UP, UP, UP. I've got to WORK, WORK, WORK."

She steps out of bed and walks lightly to the bathroom. Her perfect buttocks, sun-tanned except for a thin and wobbling white v, slip neatly from side to side. I hear the wholesome sound of the splashing and teeth cleaning that prefaces the epic scrubbings, tonings and conditionings that will come later. Still nude, she trips out of the bathroom singing *True Blue* by Madonna, a song I have come heartily to loathe.

She sits by the phone stand and dials. All I can see are her long legs and the pubic hair that looks unnaturally thick on her smooth body, a forgotten, animal region that has escaped the scrubbings, toning and conditionings. The sight causes an unwelcome commotion in my own animal region, a commotion that wakes me up far more effectively than any alarm clock.

Caro talks, talks in a way that is a sin against the hallowed slobbiness of Saturday morning.

". . . yes, David, I *know* I'm a workaholic, isn't everyone, and it's the only way to get things done. Such a busy week, wasn't it, but so much fun. How did things go yesterday? . . . Yup, we had a great time at Orso's. Barry Humphries *and* Nigel Hawthorne, all the regulars. I wanted to snap them up for the launch but Mark said he'd walk out if I went up and talked to them . . . calls himself a journalist, I don't know, I could have hit him, but I bowed to his wishes *just* this once, you know what the poor little boy can be like when he gets in a tizz . . . So who've you got . . . yes, yes . . . uh-huh, good . . . Penelope Keith, good . . . Antonia Fraser, great, the qualities will love that . . . Roger Moore, well done, fantastic, hang on, pen's run out . . ."

Soft-porn shot of Caro's bottom as she bends straight-legged to open the drawer of the cupboard. I cover my face with the duvet.

"David Steel, yes. Derek Hatton, oh come on, David. Surely . . . Yasmin Le Bon. Better. Who?" (She screeches). "YOU HAVEN'T! You STARLET! I love you! God, that's marvellous. That's good. Yes. See you Monday. You're a STAR. Ciao!"

Caro puts the phone down and dances a jog on the spot.

"Brooke Shields," she annunciates slowly. *"Brooke Shields.* Wow."

"Brooke Shields what?" I ask obediently.

"Coming to our magazine launch of course, dumbo. What else? David thinks he can get her. Think of those lovely inches!" I peep under the duvet.

"Don't be naughty. *Column* inches, big boy. Brooke . . . Brooke-Brooke Brooke-Brooke, Brooke Shields, Brooke Shields, Brooke Shields," she chants to the tune of *True Blue* and dances downstairs.

I push back the duvet and pull on my old dressing gown. On the street outside, children are shouting, executive cars are starting and the monotonous traffic noise that will last until the early hours of tomorrow morning is already audible from the Lower King's Road.

Caro returns with her tracksuit on and two mugs of camomile tea. I am made to sit on the bed and talk.

"There was something I forgot to say in the restaurant last night, mainly because Ursula was talking so much – God she goes on, but she's such a sweetie don't you think? Oh of course, she was your friend first . . . Anyway, what I wanted to say."

"What is it?"

"Don't be impatient, Marky. I remember. You remember that Lori girl? You would, as she's supposed to be an old flame of yours, you randy old Bagpuss." More playful ticklings. "Well. She's back from her travels."

"The last I heard she was in Turkey."

"Living with a man on a yacht. Yes. But that's all over, apparently. David saw her in the Soho Brasserie, looking *terrible*. Long hair, scruffy, *sandals*, would you believe."

"In a funny way, I could."

"Oh, come on. I suppose you know her better, but no one wears sandals."

"But David said he saw her wearing sandals."

"I know, but can you believe it?"

"As he said so, and as he's not a liar, then yes."

"Don't be grumpy. You know what I mean. Anyway, here is the really unbelievable part. She told him that she's planning to go and live on a commune. Organic farming, experimental lifestyle, all that! Outrageous, isn't it?"

"But you like organic farming. We've got lots of organic produce in the house."

"Yes, Mark, but actually *doing* it, can you imagine anything more horrid? David could barely stop himself laughing. Such a 1970s thing to do."

"I don't know."

"Come on, Marky. Communes. Communists. Communal toilets."

She laughs at her verbal dexterity.

"Some people think . . . I don't know."

"Come on! Communes, Mark. It's all so hippy, and you know it. Mind, you used to be a bit of a hippy yourself, didn't you, lover? I'll never forget that time we dug out those old pictures of you with your long hair and those *awful* people from wherever it is you come from, really, I nearly had my doubts. Still, we've made you into a nice, well-behaved Fulham Yuppy now, haven't we, sugar?"

Caro laughs her way to the bathroom. My stomach feels knotted and my breath feels hot on my lips. Bloody shut up, Caro. Shut up.

"So are you going to see her again? Lori?" she asks in a ridiculous, casual voice.

"I don't know. I doubt it."

"Oh, you sit-on-the-fence. Make a decision. I don't mind."

She comes back in and sees me sitting pensively on the edge of the bed. She takes pity on me, and puts her hands on my shoulders, breathing toothpaste fumes into my face.

"Come on," she says in a soft, encouraging voice. "Up and at 'em. The Famous Six for dinner tonight."

"Who?"

"Wake up! Me, you, Soapy, Julia, Sally, Rodney. The Six Musketeers. And don't forget, we've got to persuade Sally and Rodney to come to Portugal."

She heads back to the bathroom, then pauses at the door.

"And darling, you will try not to argue with Rodders again, won't you? It all got a bit boring last time."

Here it comes. There is no chance of winning, so get the fight over quickly and maybe I can go back to sleep.

"But Caro, he still hasn't apologised to me for the things he said to me in the Groucho that time. You know that. Can't you see it from my point of view?"

She sighs and leans against the door frame.

"Marky, 'that time' was six whole months ago. Ancient history. It was nothing in the first place, only Sally having a joke, it was only a joke, Sally and me were having a good girly giggle about it only the other day. Gosh, she's naughty sometimes, but what an absolute darling. You are silly and serious sometimes. Your clothes are on the chair," she says as she turns away.

On the chair is my neatly folded tracksuit, having been washed at just the right temperature, conditioned, fabric-softened and rinse-aided; and now it lies there, ready for action.

EPILOGUE

On Saturday at Abbeybrooke Parish Church, the marriage took place of Miss Caroline Serena Sophie Cox of Abbeybrooke and Mr Mark J of Fulham, London.

The bride, wearing an off-white Edwardian gown with accessories sponsored by the Mussels Health and Gourmet Club, London SW6, Your Complete Lifestyle and Foodstyle Center, was given away by her father, Group Captain Rudolph Cox, MBE, DSO.

The reception was held in the Abbeybrooke Arms, where a special 'Dynasty' wedding breakfast and cabaret offered by Mrs Norma Youell was much appreciated by family and guests alike.

The bride is a public relations executive in London. The groom, currently a journalist, says he intends to settle in Abbeybrooke and become an organic farmer.

THE END

GLOSSARY

This glossary of terms used in the book is for the
benefit of posterity, because posterity is notoriously
stupid and looks blank when you mention the most
common phrases and places. The glossary may also
recommend itself to anyone who lived on a desert
island between the years 1980-89.

Acid Hallucogenic drug that messes up the senses.
Acid House Drug-influenced dance music that messes up
parties.
Air head One unencumbered by the complexities of modern
life and thought.
Amadeus Movie that made Mozart out to be a gibbering
wally. Appealed more to gibbering wallies than devotees of
Mozart.
Anorexia Nervosa Sad 'slimming disease' invented in the
late twentieth century.

Archer, Jeffrey One of the few multi-millionaires with whom no one wants to swap places.

Armani, Georgio Designer of Italian designer clothes for designer Soho people, including designers. See Joseph, Lauren etc.

Astley, Rick Young singer whose honest, homely face is almost enough to make you forgive him for the records he makes.

Atkinson, Rowan Diminutive, versatile former James Bond extra.

Bagpuss Cuddly children's television character. cf **Howe, Sir Geoffrey.**

Barbour (→mid-1980s) Waxed cotton advert displayed in London to advertise wearer's second home in the country. (mid-1980s←) Wet weather wear as ubiquitous as the 1960s pac-a-mac.

Bass Weejun American company responsible for shodding the English media.

Beck's German beer fashionable among young drinkers who think it is American.

Bimbo In Victorian times, a form of brandy-based punch. Now a form of punch-based female.

Bint Arabic word for a young girl. Now used of bimbos (cf) who are popular with Hoorays (cf) and Arabs.

Bitch Sharp-tongued person of either sex.

Bonehead Species of English provincial male common in the mid-1970s. Characteristic markings: feather-cut hair, tank top, baggy trousers with pockets in impractical places (such as half way down the leg).

Boss, Hugo German fashion designer who expands into new areas such as toiletries. Being German, cars cannot be far behind. See Armani, Smith etc.

Bottom line In business, a term used to convey an unpleasant revelation masquerading as hard financial sense.

Braganza 1640-1910: ruling dynasty of Portugal and, later, of Brazil. 1985- : French restaurant in Soho.

Breakdancing Streetwise athletes who do things on their heads that few people can do on their feet.

Brightman, Sarah Former go-go dancer turned major international opera star.

Brilliant (of designers, chefs etc) Passably talented. (Of anything else) Quite good.

Bronson, Charles Pock-marked American star of pock-marked American films.

Budweiser Czech-American beer referred to as 'Bud' by Americans and mock-Americans; by Czechs, referred to as 'unavailable'.

Burton's Firm which makes enough dull suits to support Sir Ralph Halpern's astronomical salary and so keep the bimbo industry hoping. Do *not* see Armani, Joseph, Lauren etc.

Caine, Michael Thatcherite film star, part-owner of Langan's (cf), but very accomplished for all that.

Caprice, Le Fashionable Mayfair restaurant. **Securing a table at Le Caprice** Proof of fame or influence.

Carnaby Street Ugly London side street.

Cats The first vastly successful musical to produce not a single tune that anyone can remember.

Chanel Number 5 Odoriferous method of checking a woman's income bracket.

Chardonnay Grape variety invariably chosen at Soho lunches.

Chevignon Big French label on big French trousers.

Chilling out Tense state of mind experienced by middle-class Londoners trying to act like cool New York ghetto kids.

Church's Company which impartially shods new moneyed and old moneyed feet – any feet, indeed, as long as they are moneyed.

Coach and Horses, The Pub with mythical reputation which looks like every other pub in central London.

Cocaine Means by which the rich and insecure divert funds for arms sales to Colombia.

Colony Rooms, The Claustrophobic Soho club for superannuated Bohemians. Guests frequently suffer violent verbal abuse from members, an experience they sometimes mistake for a mystical initiation rite.

Comme des Garçons The fashion designers' designers. See Armani, Conran etc.

Conran, Jasper Designer fashion designer product of designer product designer. See Boss, Commes des Garçons etc.

Cool Temperature invented by 1940s jazzmen. Since appropriated by everyone from the lukewarm to the scorching.

Coronation Street Unfashionable television series watched by a quarter of the British population.

Costello, Elvis Founder of ex-computer programmer rock.

Currie, Edwina Politician wife of popular Midlands chartered accountant.

Cynicism Expression of mild doubt or scepticism.

Dallas American television series about rich, badly dressed people who seduce and shoot each other.

d'Arby, Terence Trent Man with a name like the hero of Jane Austen novel. Has little else in common with said hero.

Day-Lewis, Daniel English actor. Often plays unglamorous parts; source of some bemusement as a result.

Decadent Anyone who drinks at lunchtime and sometimes wears jeans to the office.

de Paul, Lyndsey Pop singer with a tenacious grip on fame considering few people can remember the lisping, slight pop songs that made her famous.

Def Definitive, quite good. Street expression used exclusively in newspapers and magazines.

Derro In Australia, a derelict or tramp. In the UK, anyone who meets with your mild disapproval.

Doorstep Front line in the newspapers' campaign against personal privacy.

Dreadlocks Tousled West Indian hairstyle unsuccessfully copied by West End hairstylists.

Dynasty American TV series about personalities who are enviable for everything except their personalities.

EastEnders Popular BBC TV series. Especially popular among popular newspapers hard up for news.

Ecstasy A mild, narcotic inflammation of the senses.

Emerson, Lake and Palmer Tedious progressive rock band whom not even a 1970s revival will rescue from oblivion.

Fatal Attraction Film dealing with the perils of adultery. Greeted with great excitement, as if it were the first time this common theme had been dramatised.

Fergie Duchess of York; bumptious royal.

Filofax Useful clerical accessory.

Floozie user of the spare toothbrush in male households.

Four letter man Three letter men are OBEs, DSOs etc. Four letter men are distinguished only by euphemism.

Fox, Samantha Topless model with homely, girl-next-door looks. To live next door to Ms Fox, however, you need to be a millionaire.

Fraser, Lady Antonia Middle-brow writer and upper-middle-brow socialist.

Gel All-purpose substance used throughout the 1980s, most commonly on hair. Contact with strong lights (eg, in night-clubs) produces an odd chemical reaction.

Geldof, Bob Hairy Irish saint and pop star who writes hairy songs which, sadly, no one listens to anymore.

Glitter, Gary Ludicrous 1970s pop star. Not so ludicrous that he couldn't make money out of sensible young people in the 1980s, however.

Grayson, Larry Camp comedian of long ago.

Greer, Germaine Pretty Australian writer, inspiration of countless acts of gallantry from Italian men.

Groucho Club, The Club for people who can't join other clubs because other clubs wouldn't have them as a member.

Guinness, Sir Alec Fine English actor and gentleman who has no place in this book.

Hack A writer of newspapers, a harmless drudge.

Hang in there Make a complete pest of yourself while under the false impression that you are being gritty and heroic.

Harper's and Queen Sporting magazine that covers the hunt; the hunting of old money by new.

Hatton, Derek Little-known PR (cf) executive.

Helvin, Maria Hawaiian model and television presenter, chief fantasy figure of rubbernecking businessmen.

Hip Hop Violent twitching brought on by over-exposure to electronic percussion. Similar ailments include **House, Garage, New Jersey, Belgian New Beat.**

Hawthorne, Nigel Pin-striped actor.

Hooray Rich, exhibitionist young man with very little of worth to exhibit.

Howe, Sir Geoffrey Statesman and all-round harmless old geezer. Private life a model of propriety.

Humphries, Barry Australian impressionist. His popular

characters include 'Dame Edna Everage', 'Sir Les Patterson' and 'Clive James'.

Hunk Thick slice of manhood.

Jones, Grace Disco singer with robotic voice and very human figure.

Jones, Indiana Hero of popular adventure film series. Re-launched distressed leather jackets and distressed blonde heroines.

Joseph Expensive clothes shop. See Armani, Conran etc.

K Unit of material wealth and linguistic poverty.

Karma Serene state of mind brought about by believing psycho-mystical bullshit.

Keith, Penelope Floral print actress.

Kettner's Famous Soho restaurant where Oscar Wilde used to seduce young men. Now sells hamburgers and pizzas and provides a venue for middle-ranking young executives to seduce each other.

Kevin Generic name for common English tribe distinguished by their highlighted hair, white socks and grey shoes.

Krug Champagne journalists order when someone else is paying. See **Public Relations**.

Kryptonite Substance that does to Superman what estate agents do to dinner party conversations.

Krystel, Sylvie French actress and anatomy teacher who influenced a generation of teenage males.

Langan's Brasserie Celebrity restaurant where the customers are fed indifferent food. The customers then willingly allow themselves to be fed to waiting photographers.

Lauren, Ralph Expensive American fashion designer. See Armani, Joseph etc.

Le Bon, Yasmin Model wife of tubby pop star.

Lee-Lewis, Jerry American rock 'n' roll star who, like Charlie Chaplin and Romeo before him, caused a stir by marrying a very young girl.

Lennox, Annie Peroxided pop singer; a combination of feminist and *femme fatale*.

Liberty London department store for people who can afford to shop in Harrod's but have too much taste to do so.

Lig To attend a party given by a person or organisation who does not know, like, respect or care for you.

Lightweight Term used to denote anyone who might threaten one's own professional or personal advancement.

Limelight Club Converted church not noticeably popular among converts to the church.

Lovin' Spoonful Dreamy US group of the late 1960s. Once laughable, now revered.

Lusardi, Linda Topless model with homely, sultry-temptress-next-door looks.

Ma Cuisine Homely French restaurant in un-homely Covent Garden side street.

Madonna Religious leader; worshipped by the notorious Rebellious Teenage Girl sect.

Mellor, David Man who made a fortune out of designing forks and saucepans; the kind of thing that could only happen in the 1980s.

Melly, George English jazz singer, colourful enough not to mind that contradiction in terms.

Mexican Wave Exercise invented by crowds watching the 1986 World Cup. Sections of the crowd stand up in turn, producing a spectacle which is usually preferable to events on the pitch.

Michael, George Hairy English pop star who writes clean-shaven songs.

Mick (Jagger) and Jerry (Hall) Jet-set partnership that marked the demise of the Rolling Stones and their singer as a healthily destructive force in society.

Minogue, Kylie Youthful Australian actress, singer and political thinker. When asked her opinions on the South Africa problem, she is reported to have said, "I don't think they should shoot the rhinos."

Moore, Dudley Diminutive ex-comedian and support act to satirist Peter Cook.

Morrison, Jim Romantic, dead hippy figure who wrote romantic lines such as "hello, I love you, won't you tell me your name?"

Naff Term used to denote garbage by garbage collectors.

Negative Disagreement with my intelligent and incisive point of view.

New man Subject of a brave experiment to reverse 3,000 years of indoctrination within the space of a single decade.

Northern Soul Unlikely alliance of Memphis and Wigan forged in the 1970s.

Orso's Like Le Caprice (cf) without the waiting list.

Owen, David Husband of well-known literary agent.

Palladium, The West End retirement home.

Paparazzi Archangels of rubbernecking.

Perrier Standard late 1980s question: "Whatever did we do before Perrier?" Answer: water came from taps.

Pet Shop Boys Purveyors of camp music to teenage girls.

Phantom of the Opera, The Featherweight Andrew Lloyd-Webber musical for people who dislike opera.

Philosophy Method of working as expounded by commercial organisations.

Princess of Wales Model royal.

Private Eye Trade magazine of the legal profession.

Public Relations (PR) Scientific breakthrough whereby journalists absorb highly selective information through glasses of alcohol.

Puff i) Discredited word for male homosexual. ii) Newspaper story resulting from scientific experiment involving journalist, PR executive and bottle of Krug (ccf).

Punk (pre-1976) Second-rate, inferior person. (1976-80) First-rate, radical hero. (1980-) Second-rate, inferior person.

Puttnam, David Bearded, caring English film producer. Sacked by Hollywood for having a beard and not caring enough about Hollywood.

Python, Monty BBC comedy programme, very amusing in fits, worshipped by engineering students.

Rice, Anneka Goofy TV personality who promotes helicopters and large bottoms.

Ridgeley, Andrew Pop singer, formerly one half of Wham, now one half of not very much.

Ronnie Scott's Jazz club for aged and youthful wearers of turtle-neck sweaters.

Ross, Jonathan Polite young man from Romford who asks rude questions on television.

Rotary Societies Clubs for men with insufficient funds, imagination and kinkiness to join the Freemasons.

Rottweiler Dogs which became very popular in the 1980s among dim-witted or insecure types short of bark or bite.

Rowe, Erica A woman who took off her shirt at a rugby match and became extremely famous as a result.

Rubbernecks Urban individuals noted for their vanity, arrogance, affluence, youth (real and pretended), promiscuity, neurosis, aggression, good looks (genuine and manufactured), sociability, clothes obsession, lack of thoughtfulness, suppleness of morality, suppleness of spine.

Russell, Ken English film director; he hits people who say rude things about him.

SAS Souped-up squaddies who have become folk heroes among the feeble-witted.

Saatchi, Charles Millionaire English advertising man who advertised the Conservative Party, then bought an art collection.

Sexy Commercially viable.

Shields, Brooke Model American actress.

Slag Word for promiscuous woman, most often used abusively by promiscuous man.

Sleep, Wayne Model dancer.

Sloane Square Nature reserve in London SW1.

Smash Hits Teenage pop magazine not written by teenage pop fans.

Smith, Mandy Independent young actress doubling as an exercise course for ageing rock 'n' roll stars. See **Wyman, Bill.**

Smith, Mel Portly, balding comedian who does not tell portly, balding comedian jokes.

Smith, Paul Menswear consultant to Marks and Spencer. See also Lauren, Armani etc.

Smoke, The Old-fashioned slang word for London never used by Londoners.

Soho Brasserie Bar that accurately reproduces the conditions of an underground train carriage during the rush hour.

Spielberg, Stephen Bearded, caring American director worshipped by Hollywood.

Sugar Daddy Generous older man. Not necessarily Bill Wyman.

Sweet Credulous; naive; non-threatening. (Of tradesmen) Underpaid.

Tart Healthy opportunist of either sex.

Taylor, Elizabeth Screen goddess who has been known to do herself rather too well on the ambrosia and nectar.

Thatcher, Margaret Prime Minister and spiritual leader of a fanatical cult of 1980s people who deserted their homes in search of Fulfilment, Meaning and £100 K a year.

Top of the Pops The kind of nice party your parents would like you to go to when you're a teenager.

Tutton's Covent Garden bistro where the less aspiring sort of young professionals try to seduce Italian tourists. See **Kettner's.**

Type B personality One who suppresses his or her emotions. Term probably invented in America – surprisingly, as this characteristic is unknown there.

Veggie (pre-1985) Term of contempt for vegetarians. (post-1985) Term of approbation for one quarter of London's restaurant-going population.

Waugh, Auberon Literary journalist and massage connoisseur whose popularity among the repressed classes stems from his frequent use of words like 'tart' and 'cretin'.

Weymouth, Viscount Hippy, party-going aristocrat. With long hair and beard, looks like one of his own medieval ancestors.

Williams, John Composer of a single, stirring theme, subsequently used in about 200 different movies.

Wilson, A.N. Tweedy novelist and critic.

Wogan BBC showcase for new books, films etc. Origin of title unknown.

Workaholic Anyone in full-time, white-collar employment

during the 1980s. Also, title claimed by some who weren't (cf. **Fergie**).

Wyman, Bill Father figure to aspiring young female models and singers. Also bass player with the Rolling Stones, arthritis permitting. See **Smith, Mandy**.

Yo! Convivial greeting originally used in Jamaica, New York and Bristol.

Yuppy The only endangered species which the Caring Nineties will *not* try to save.

Zanzibar, The i) Fashionable, elegant Covent Garden club. ii) Outdated dive on the borders of Holborn.

Zazou Media persons' restaurant and bar between Channel Four and Saatchi and Saatchi. (vb) To discuss salaries over lunch.